S0-AGV-082

# A Storyteller's

# GHOST STORIES

by

Duane Hutchinson

Foundation Books
Box 29229
Lincoln, Nebraska 68529

Second Printing, 1987



ISBN 0-934988-32-3

Published by Foundation Books
P. O. Box 29229
Lincoln, Nebraska 68529
Printed and bound in the United States of America

This book is dedicated
to Travis Hackel
who said,
after I told him the story
of the woman with the golden arm,
"Tell it again."
I told it again.
"Now, I've got it!"
And he did have it too,
for he told it again and again to his friends.

# TABLE OF CONTENTS

# INTRODUCTION

One way to insure a loud, joyful response from a group of grade school children is to ask, "Would you like to hear a ghost story?" They yell and stomp and beg for "a scary one."

Why, I often wonder, do children universally beg for scary stories? Is it like a roller coaster ride of the spirit? Is it for the pleasure of a tickling down the spine? Is it a yearning to understand more of the life of the spirit?

I believe we could answer yes to all of those questions. In our materialistic society, we have often denied hunger for talk of spiritual things. Mystery has been edged out of our time. Weather used to be a mystery, and now nightly we hear pragmatic discussions of low pressure areas and cyclonic winds.

The most frequent question asked by children after the telling of a story is this: "Is that true? Is that a real story? Sometimes, if I want to hedge, I answer, "It is true that it is a story." And this sparks a discussion about how words can be twisted to mean different things.

Ghost stories have always been enjoyable for me. If I had ever seen a ghost and been thoroughly frightened, the stories would not be as much fun. Some of my happiest moments have been telling ghost stories and animal stories with a group of young people around a campfire out in the woods or in a dormitory room on a college campus. The students at the university used to empty out one of the rooms, haul in mattresses wall-to-wall and sprawl as they do for TV. After stories come discussions.

"Have you ever seen a ghost?" is a frequent question.

"No, I haven't," I answer, "but I take people seriously who tell me their stories." Many of the stories I have collected come from people who believe the experience, even if they can't explain it.

I have deliberately not collected stories from people who are too self-assured about what it all means and who have ready answers for all questions. I have not collected stories of violence. I don't believe that immortals have any more right to violence than mortals do and I will not give them the time of day--or night.

I have avoided the occult. It is dark and depressing to me. Some people have had their minds messed up by dwelling on the occult. I want the Good Spirit. I like stories such as of the Ghost of Montecelli who is seeking to reveal truth. I am drawn to the Ghost of Nebraska Wesleyan who was seeking and sharing music. I often tell people after the story, "She never hurt anyone. She was a respected musician and a sensitive artist. I hope she has had pleasure in heaven over the enjoyment hundreds of people have had over her story."

My goal is the joy of a good shiver and that none of these stories hurts anybody. Rumors are that a ghost in a house might make it difficult to sell. It would have to bean evil or threatening ghost, and I haven't collected those kinds of stories. Where I thought residents might be made uncomfortable, I have altered names and identifying facts.

This is not a documentary. It is a story book.

I wish to thank the many people who have given me ghost stories. Most of them did not wish to have their name mentioned, but still wanted to have their story told. They, as I, enjoy the story for the story's sake. Thank you.

I am grateful to my son, Steve Hutchinson, for reading this manuscript, pointing out errors, and making many valuable suggestions.

And thanks most of all to my wife, Marilyn, who has faithfully edited all I have written. She has put books into final form for the publisher. We have had fun working together. While she is not a ghost story enthusiast, she has been willing to help me fulfill a dream. Without her, none of my books would have been possible.

We would lie side by side
In the old iron bed
And make up stories,
My brother and I.

We would curl our toes
Around the little monster head
That gripped the welded bed
Irons in its teeth.

"Eeeiiooh," my brother would say;
"Hoooiieee" I would say in return.

"Look at the attic door," he would say.
I had already looked at it.
"The door is lifting up
By unseen hands," he would say.
I already knew that.
Somewhere in the cold attic
Dusty figures
Opened treasure chests
And dropped the lids.
They moved heavy boxes,
Dressed themselves
In the veils of threadbare curtains,
And fancied themselves
In broken mirrors.
But the worst
Was when they
Lurched against the door--
The attic door--
That separated the living
From the dead.
They gently lifted--
Oh, so carefully lifted,
Sucked up with mildewed breath
The door above our bed,
Then let it drop again.

"Eeeiioooh," said my brother;
"Hoooiieee," I said in return.

-Duane Hutchinson

# THE GOLDEN ARM

When I was a little boy I heard this story. It was the first ghost story I had ever heard--at least the first one that I can remember.

I not only remember this story, but have continued to tell it ever since. A few years ago a university student, Russ Roberts, found it in an anthology attributed to Mark Twain. It was a thrill for me to see how close my story was to Twain's. And, after all, I had heard it from another small boy--an undependable source--and had been reshaping it as I told it all these years. Oral history wins again! Sort of.

Mark Twain is supposed to have gotten his story from black people around Hannibal. Was it of African origin? Perhaps all things came out of Africa. But, since that time, I've found a version of it in a collection of 18th Century English fairy tales.

Here it goes, as I heard it and have retold it. Let me warn you. It has power. Some listeners claim to have nightmares after hearing it.

Once upon a time there lived an old man and an old woman who loved each other very much. They got along quite well for many years until one day she had a terrible accident. Her arm was cut off.

She turned to her husband and said, "Henry? Would you make me a new arm?"

He said, "Because I love you so much, Effie, I will make you a beautiful golden arm."

So, he took all his savings to town and bought gold enough to make her a beautiful golden arm. That was before the price of gold had gone up.

She was so proud of that arm that wherever she went she laid her arm across her lap and tugged up her sleeve so people could see more of her golden arm.

They got along well for many more years, until she grew so old and feeble she was afraid she was going to die.

She said, "Henry? If I die before you die, will you bury me--*with* my golden arm?"

Henry said, "Effie, if you die before I die, I'll bury you with your golden arm."

One night she died and Henry was faithful to her. He buried her with her golden arm.

But some months after this, one night the old man lay in bed all alone thinking how old and how poor he was. He was so poor he hardly had money enough to buy food.

"Why am I so poor?" he asked himself. "I worked hard all my life. I saved my money. Ah! I know why I'm poor! I spent all my savings on that golden arm. It's not doing anybody any good. Effie can't even use it anymore.

(**Now, roll your eyes from side to side and look guiltily toward the windows.**)

"I think I'll go and dig it up!"

Now, he knew he wasn't supposed to do that. He knew he wasn't supposed to dig where he wasn't supposed to. But, he sneaked out the back door anyway in his long black coat. He went out to the shed behind the house and grabbed his sharpest shovel. He hid it under his long black coat. He looked around.

(**Here you roll your eyes again, crouch over and pretend to hide something under your coat.**)

Nobody was watching him. So, he started to run. And he ran and he ran and he ran. (**I crouch over and look around behind me while making the motions of running.**)

When he came to the big iron fence he grabbed the iron gate and pulled it open. "Eeeeeek." (**Make a good squeaky gate sound by starting the Eeee with a high falsetto and ending with low throat sounds.**) He pulled the gate back on its rusty hinges.

As soon as he squeezed through he pushed the gate shut. "Eeeeek. Klunk."

He ran and ran again until he came to the very place where the golden arm was buried. He started to dig. "Scrape. Scrape. Scrape."

He stopped. He looked around. Nobody watching.

He dug again. "Scrape. Scrape. Scrape."

The moon came out from under a cloud and illuminated the whole landscape. He stopped digging and looked around. Surely somebody could see him out there, digging where he wasn't supposed to be digging. But, no faces looked through the fence.

He kept on digging. "Scrape. Scrape. Bump!"

He had hit the top of the box. He kept on digging, "Scrape. Scrape. Scratch." All around the edge of the lid he dug, until he had the lid loose.

Then, he reached his fingers over the edge of the lid. It was mossy and mouldy and rotten. He pulled up the lid. "Eeeeeek." Pulled it up on its rusty hinges.

Up with the lid came cobwebs and spider webs.

Down inside the box he could see the golden arm glistening in the moonlight. He reeeeeached down into the box and GRABBED IT! (**Here you scream like crazy as you shout out the last two words.**)

He grabbed it and pulled it loose. Threw it off to one side.

Looked around again. Nobody watching him. So, he grabbed the top of the box, pulled it down. "Eeeeek. Clump."

He picked up the golden arm. It was wet and dewy and mossy. He hid it under his coat. He picked up his shovel, scraped all the dirt back in the hole so nobody could tell he had been there and hid the shovel under his coat.

He started to run. He ran and ran and ran until he arrived at the gate. (**Imitate the crouched over position and motions of running, while looking around behind you.**)

He took hold of the iron gate and pulled it back. "Eeeeeek." He ran through and pulled the gate shut. "Eeeeek. Clank."

He ran and ran down the road, hoping nobody could see him.

Then he heard it. Something coming down the road behind him.

He ran faster and faster.

It was coming faster. "Who's got my golden arm?"

He ran and ran until he came to his house. He didn't take time to put the shovel away. He shoved it under the house.

"Who's got my golden arm?"

He ran into the house and slammed the door. Pulled the bolt across. Safe!

"Who's got my golden arm?" The voice came around the eaves of the house like the wind.

He ran into the bedroom, carrying the golden arm with him.

"Who's got my golden arm?" came around the corners of the bedroom.

He jumped into bed. Pushed the golden arm under the pillow to keep it safe.

"Who's got my golden arm?"

It was getting closer. He pulled up the covers over his face to shut out the sound. But, he couldn't shut out the sound.

"Who's got my golden arm?"

It sounded as if it had climbed into the bedroom with him. He pulled back the corner of the covers so he could get one eyeball out to look. (**You can act this out, circling fingers around an eye.**)

A hand was reaching in through the window. It wasn't even breaking the glass. "Who's got my golden arm?" came right with it.

The arm reached over the bed.

"Who's got my--YOU GOT IT!!!"

It is important in telling this story to interrupt your own "Who's got my golden arm?" If you wait 'til the end, nobody will jump. But if you catch them in the middle, your listeners will come right out of their seats.

# THE GHOST OF THE LILAC PERFUME

Once when I visited Lincoln High School and told ghost stories, a tall senior came up to me after class and told me a story. I never made a note, yet I remembered it later. The story had a kind of completeness and closure which made it easily remembered. Here it is:

When my family moved to Beatrice several years ago, we moved into a big house that had a lot of steps running down from the front door to the sidewalk.

We soon discovered that we couldn't get our cats to cross the third step. We'd go out to feed the cats at the front door. We'd call them but they wouldn't come up any closer than the third step from the top. We'd have to step down, pick up the cats and lift them over.

After awhile we noticed that whenever we leaned over to pick up the cats we could smell lilac perfume. There weren't any lilacs around. And, anyway, it wasn't the season for lilacs.

Then, one time, my sister was up during the night and happened to walk past the front door. She looked through the glass panel in the door and saw something that made her scream.

She screamed and screamed until my parents woke up and all of us kids ran downstairs to see what was happening. We found her pointing out the door, down at those steps.

It was awful. There was an old woman lying on that third step. Her head was bent off at an angle so that you knew she had a broken neck and you knew she was dead.

But only half of our family could see it and half of us couldn't. I could see it. My mother couldn't. My father could see it and wanted to call the police. My mom said, "No! Don't call the police--they'll think we're a bunch of nuts. Nothing's out there."

There on the third step was that old body with the neck bent--I couldn't stand to look at it, but I couldn't help peeking out either.

Mom pulled Dad back from the phone. "Don't call anybody!" she said. "Let's try to get calmed down. I'll make some hot chocolate."

We stayed in the kitchen talking 'til daylight. We looked out and--nothing there! The steps were clear.

Dad went to the neighbors next door as soon as they were up. Asked them about it. They didn't know anything that could explain what had happened. But they had only lived in the house for three years.

"Why don't you go visit the old man that used to live in our house?"

"Good idea."

So, we drove across town that morning and visited the man in a nursing home. When we described the old woman on the steps and how she was dressed, he said, "Oh yes! I knew her well. We lived next door for thirty years. She always kept a lot of cats."

"Really? We have cats too."

"You might as well say it was the cats that killed her."

"They attacked her?"

"Oh, no," the old man said. "She'd always feed those cats out on the front steps. They'd spill their waterpan and there'd always be ice out there in winter.

"I remember the night she died. She must have slipped on the landing outside the front door. Fell down the steps and broke her neck, I guess. I remember when the ambulance came and got her. Picked her up off the third step.

"I always claimed the cats tipped over the water pan and she slipped on the ice. Whatever it was, it sure ended her career right then and there."

We were all breathless, waiting for more.

"What else do you remember about her?"

"Well, let me think." He rubbed his chin and chuckled a little. "I remember one thing. She always wore perfume real strong. You get downwind of her and you'd smell it all right. Yessir! Lilac perfume. I can smell it yet."

And so could we.

## RANDY

Randy, a high school student, seventeen years old, told me this story. He said over and over, "I want you to have this story." To me it is filled with pain and beauty and I have told it reverently to many children.

Much more there is to it than I can tell here. I have changed names and identifying facts to protect his family's privacy. His father is a leader in his profession, his mother was an active woman in the community and home. I hope that Randy, a talented writer, will someday go on himself to tell more of his story.

On January 7th, 1976, my Mom was killed in a plane crash north of Fairbury, Nebraska. We had been on vacation, visiting our relatives in Los Angeles. That afternoon we refueled our Beech Barron at Farmington, New Mexico. When we came over Hill City, Kansas, Dad became concerned about visibility ahead, so he radioed for Lincoln, Omaha and St. Joseph weather reports.

At six-thirty we crossed the Nebraska line with fog and clouds socking us in. The instruments indicated we were at the assigned altitude, but in reality we were flying only a few feet off the ground. At 6:42 we hit ground in a prairie pasture, slid 200 yards, sheared off a wing on a tree and came to a stop.

Mom had unbuckled her seat belt only seconds before, so she could turn back and help one of the children. As we struck, she was thrown forward. At that instant the propeller on the left engine sheared off and came through the window, striking her in the head. Her body was thrown through the windshield so far out in the field Dad didn't even find her for half an hour.

All of us had injuries--Dad and us four children. Dad and I worked to get everyone out in case of fire. Dad and I both went to a nearby highway to find help. He waved his flashlight repeatedly at passing cars, but no one stopped. When he saw we weren't going to get help right away, and that the plane wasn't going to burn, he lifted us back into the cabin and covered the children with blankets. It was the little he could do to keep us warm for the night and forstall shock.

We were there nine and a half hours before help came. And then it was two inebriated bachelor brothers who came across the field. They were on their way home from a night in the pool hall. In their stumbling way, they got us to an emergency room of a nearby hospital. But it was 2:30 the next afternoon before we arrived at Lincoln General Hospital--and only then thanks to the help of the National Guard's helicopters and the cooperation of many people.

By the way, Dad became especially concerned after the accident about care of trauma victims. He worked hard to bring about changes in the way emergency rooms handle patients.

For three months I remembered very little of the accident. Then my memory came back and with it, terrible nightmares.

I had never been able to describe a dream. Dreams were not that specific for me. Yet, three months after the accident I started having the "crash" dream over and over. In real life it had been only the crashing and the sliding--like being inside a trash compactor. It seemed as if it was taking forever, but, of course, it was only seconds. Every one had been silent as we were grinding to a stop. Now, in the dream there were screams.

Worst of all, the dream kept repeating itself. We would go through the long crash and then it would back up, like the "Brady Bunch" where the ball keeps coming down again and again, we kept crashing.

One night I was sleeping in my own bedroom where we live out in the country and the dream started, then repeated, and repeated. When we crashed for the third time, something came and hit me in the face. I stood up and a metal object from the plane hit me, "Bam!"

I had hit my head on the back part of the bed--the bedpost, someway. I sat up, sweating. My pajamas were clinging to me.

I looked over to the right of my bed and I could see my mother. She was beautiful, the way she was before the accident. Light shone around her, like daytime. She was coming through a tunnel of bright clouds. Yet, the light didn't shine on the walls. The bedroom, otherwise, was still dark.

At first as she came toward me, there was no expression on her face, but as she moved toward me a smile came slowly to her lips and eyes. She reached and touched her hand to my cheek. A distinct electrical charge came from her--very pleasant. I know the feeling of electricity. I once stuck a brass key into an electrical outlet. That was terrible. This flow of energy from my mother was sweet and good.

I could see tears in her eyes, but they were not sad tears. It was joy. Have you ever seen a person so happy that the person cries? It was like that. My mother's face after crying with joy. You know what I mean? The tears were still in her eyes, but the joy and relaxation were there.

She was wearing a gown, like the gown we buried her in. Never had I seen her wear anything like that. It was a gown bought especially for the funeral.

A brilliant whiteness was behind her, like a round cave, a tunnel in white clouds. It was as though the sun were shining through. The light was as daytime, normal light, not a strain to see, and afterward my eyes didn't have to adjust to the darkness in the room.

It was as if she were there all the time, but phased in and phased out. The curtains were closed in my room, the room was dark, yet I could see her as if she were in daytime. Still, the light around her didn't illuminate the walls of the room.

I watched until the vision was completed. She moved slowly back, still facing me, moving away, but not as if she were walking . . She was drawn away, through the shining tunnel. When she left it was as if she were two hundred yards away from me, even though my bedroom is only fifteen feet across or so.

At first I had been afraid, but when she touched me I felt peaceful. I slept then, better than I ever had for three months. I really began to get well from that point.

You know, Mom always had time for us. She was involved in a lot of things--taught Sunday School, was active in Auxiliary, Extension Club, bowling, and much more. But if I came to her where she was presiding over a meeting, she'd stop everything and take me up on her lap, and give me her attention.

Now, I knew she had given me her attention again when I needed her. She had come in a blaze of shining light and touched me with healing. It was as if she said, "Randy, you can go ahead and live."

# THE GHOST OF THE GRANDFATHER CLOCK

I had been telling ghost stories for ten weeks at Centennial School, Utica, Nebraska. It was the second to the last day, so, I thought, I'll tell ghost stories. I'll soon be leaving town anyway.

After class a crowd of students gathered around, each one wanting to share a ghost story. A fifth-grade girl pressed forward, looked at me with wide, frightened eyes, and said, "Mister, we had one in our house."

This is her story.

My mom likes to collect antiques. Mom buys them and Daddy refinishes them and makes them work. One of the things she wanted was a grandfather clock. Then, one day, she heard there was one for sale over at Beaver. (That's Beaver Crossing, Nebraska.)

She went over to Beaver, but she didn't like the clock. It had an unhappy face.

"What do you mean, an unhappy face," I asked. "A clock face is a clock face."

Oh, no, she said, it had a face painted on the face. The eyes rolled to one side, the lips curled down. It looked so miserable my mom didn't want it.

But, nobody else wanted it either, 'cause nobody bid on it.

After while the auctioneer said to Mom, "Mrs. Zimmerman, would you please help me? Help me get this bidding started? You go to a lot of these sales and we help each other."

So Mom bid five dollars on a clock she didn't want, nobody bid against her, and so she brought a grandfather clock home for five dollars!

Daddy teased her for bringing such an unhappy clock home. But he helped her set it up in the hallway between the dining room and the kitchen.

We hadn't had the clock very long before we heard whispering in the hallway.

"Whispering?" I asked.

It was coming from the clock. You would walk past it and hear it.

"You mean," I said, "you could hear the wheels going around inside?"

No. That's what Daddy said at first. "It's just the clock works inside."

But Mom heard it too. It was words. They didn't make any sense, but they were words. "You go up one side and down the other. Cross the seven. Move through the other side and down through . . ." It simply didn't make any sense.

It's like my little sister, Jennie, when she talks in her sleep. She talks and uses words, but the words don't make any sense.

Every one of us heard the clock, but Dad. He laughed. He wanted to tease us about it at first. Daddy said, "You're all shook up because the clock looks so unhappy."

He thought it was funny until one day it happened to him. He was walking through from the dining room to the kitchen and he jumped aside.

"Hey!" he said, and stared at the clock. "I heard it. A man was standing by the clock. He said something to me. But now--now that I look, nobody is there!"

"See, Daddy?" we said. "That's what we told you but you wouldn't believe us."

Daddy stood looking at the clock awhile and said, "Maybe it's dry. It needs oiling. I'll take it apart some day and oil it. Put it back together again. Then it won't whisper any more."

But the whispers weren't from the clock alone. We knew that. In fact, we were all getting so jittery, we didn't want to go into the dining room by ourselves. It was always: "Hey Jennie? Would you go with me? I'm going into the dining room."

Daddy didn't like that. He said, "I don't want any room in the house to be a place where the children are afraid to go by themselves."

One night at supper in the dining room, Jennie began to cry. Mom said, "What is it, Jennie? Do you have a pain?"

"No, Mom."

"Well, what is it?"

"I don't like it. I don't like to be stared at."

Mom said, "Honey, nobody's staring at you."

Jennie whirled around and pointed. "That clock!" she said, and started crying all over again.

We all knew what Jennie was talking about.

"Make him go away," Jennie said. She still stared at the clock.

Mom looked at Daddy. Daddy's neck turned red the way it does when he's mad. I knew they were going to do something.

Daddy said, "We're either going to get rid of that clock or call a priest.

One night, we were all watching TV in the dining room and Daddy stood up.

"Look at that clock!" he said.

We all looked at it. The face was changing. The eyes were rolling to the other side. The lips were curling down--it was awful.

Daddy got mad. He went to a drawer in the kitchen and brought back a screwdriver. He unscrewed the clockface until he got it off and held it in his hands.

"Look at it," he said, and held it up for us to see. "It's just pieces of tin. Now, let's not get so excited."

But, Daddy was the one that was excited that time.

He kept fussing with the clock and taking off more pieces until he had it all spread out on the dining room table. "Oil it," he said. "Oil it good and it won't be whispering any more."

We had to eat our meals in the kitchen for a week until Daddy got that clock put back together.

Then it worked fine, but . . . It still whispered.

We were getting more and more jittery.

Then, one Saturday night was a big basketball game at Seward. All of us like basketball except Mom. Mom doesn't care about it that much so she said she was going to stay home and work on a dress.

The trouble was, the only place Mom could work on the dress was in the dining room. That was where she could plug in the sewing machine and spread everything out on the table.

As we were going out the door, Daddy stuck his head back in and said, "Mother? Are you sure you don't want one of us to stay here with you?"

"Go on!" Mom waved us out the door. "Go on! You're late already. I'll be all right. Go on to the game."

"Okay? You're sure?"

Mom said she was sure so we went on.

It was a great game. We were ahead and then they were ahead. We forgot all about Mom. The score was tied at the half when we went to get popcorn and drinks.

When we came back, the third quarter started. We got a score and they got a score. Then someone blew the whistle and stopped the game. Up at the scoreboard where the men sit at a desk, one man held up a telephone and was talking. Then he picked up the microphone and said, "Ladies and gentleman! May I have your attention. We have a emergency message. Will the Clyde Zimmermans please return home immediately. Will the Zimmermans please return home immediately. There is an emergency."

Daddy jumped up and said, "The house is on fire!"

We ran out of the gym, stumbling over people, and Daddy drove home so fast we thought he was going to kill us all. We took every corner on two wheels.

We came into the yard in a cloud of dust. Daddy jumped out. As we ran to the house he said, "I don't see any smoke."

In the kitchen Mom was hanging on the edge of the sink. Her fingers were gripped over the edge and she was hysterical, shaking all over and crying.

Daddy put his arm around her. "What's wrong? What's wrong?" he kept saying, but all Mom could do was cry. She couldn't speak. I'd never seen her like that before.

Daddy made her sit down in a chair and he rubbed her back.

At last she got her voice back a little. "I was working in the dining room. Working on my dress. I was happy. Then I saw something moving. I looked up. There was a patch of light moving across the wall. I thought at first you were coming home early. Thought it was the reflection of your headlights on the wall as you came in the driveway."

Mom started crying again. Daddy rubbed her back some more.

Mom said, "I looked at the patch of light and realized it couldn't be coming from the driveway. Wrong side of the house. I put my hand up in the light until I could see my shadow on the wall. I followed the light down with my hand until I saw the light was coming to the clock. The door of the clock was opening slowly and picking up the light from the chandelier. It was moving the reflection slowly across the wall."

That was when Mom lost her cool and called the gym.

Daddy paced around. He looked at the clock and opened the door several times. "I oiled the clock," he said. "I oiled the hinges. Probably it's tipped forward a little and the latch came unhooked. The door eased open."

Then Daddy said, "That's it! I'm going to take that clock out of this house, take it to town in the pickup and sell it. First thing, Monday morning."

Mom said, "I'm going to call Father Schmitz."

She did, and she invited him for Sunday dinner the next day. During the meal we laughed and talked and laughed some more.

"Children?" Daddy said. "Do you realize what is happening?"

"What's happening?" we asked.

"We are laughing! We haven't laughed in this house for months. It was good to have the minister come eat with us."

After the meal, Father Schmitz walked over to the clock and took out a little black book. He read the most beautiful words over that clock. He even sprinkled water on it. When he was through, the clock even had a nicer look on its face. I know it was just my imagination. But anyway, it didn't whisper any more.

"Really?" I said. "It never did whisper again?"

Well, once, she said.

"What happened?" I asked, breathlessly.

The clock stopped whispering. No one stared at us from the clock any more. Jennie wasn't afraid to go into the dining room alone any more. The clock was only a clock--nothing more.

One of the things I marvelled at, as I heard this Utica fifth grader tell her story, was how her face changed with the telling. I have often seen this, but seldom so distinctly. As she told the first part of the story with the clock troubles, her expression was dark and her features pinched. But now as she reached the end, the sunshine came into her features. Her muscles relaxed and her eyes shone happily.

"But, you said it whispered once more?" I asked.

Well, she said, there was something about six weeks ago.

"Would you tell me, please?"

Mom was home alone. All of us kids were at school. Daddy was working down at the neighbors'.

Mom had a ten o'clock hair appointment in town. She wanted to finish out the egg case to take with her. When she came back from the henhouse and loaded the eggs, she came back into the house to put on her good shoes and hat and coat.

When she came through the dining room to the kitchen, past the clock, she heard a whispering. Mom jumped. She could hear real plain: "Don't go! Don't go!"

Mom backed away from the clock. "I won't go. I won't go," she said. She went to the telephone and cancelled her appointment with the hairdresser. When she hung up the phone she realized she had been talking to the clock just as if it were a person.

That scared Mom. She called Daddy at the neighbors and said, "Come home, quick! I need to talk to you," she said.

Daddy said that they were planning to have lunch for him there at noon and couldn't she tell him that night?

She said "No. I need to tell you what's happening."

Daddy said, "Can't you tell me over the telephone?"

"No!" Mom said. "Not on a party line. You come home!" She told him she had cancelled her hair appointment in town and was going to stay right there until he came home.

In about half an hour Daddy called home. He was upset. "Oh, thank God!" he said. "You didn't go to town."

Mom said, "I told you I cancelled my hair appointment and I was staying right here. Why are you so upset?"

"The bridge!" he said. "The bridge you would have gone over on the way to town.."

"What about it?"

"It has just collapsed!" Daddy said. "It's all fallen down into the bottom. You would have been killed."

The fifth grader now looked at me with big solemn eyes.

"So, we feel like it's a friendly clock now, Mister. It saved my mom's life."

That little girl's story became one of my favorites over the next few years. I told it to thousands of youngsters--and oldsters. An antique dealer in Iowa looked up a clock in his catalog and showed me the ugly face. "There's the sun and moon and stars over the top of the face. And the face does change every season. The eyes are painted on a wheel that turns behind the clock face. So, the eyes do roll to the other side looking for the new season."

When I went back to Utica three years later, I looked forward to finding the little fifth grader, now an eighth grader. But, strangely, no one knew who she was. They remembered the story, because I had come back and told it the next week.

"There was a family of Zimmermans," one boy said, "who moved over from Beaver Crossing. But they moved away soon after that."

I'd like to look up that girl and tell her thank you.

# THE CHILD IN THE NIGHTSHIRT

The first story I got from a college student came from a Hastings sophomore. This was in the early 1960's. He had worked on the Hastings Tribune that summer, he said, and for radio station KHAS. Here's his story:

I was working the night shift--a rainy and miserable night. The wind was up and slapping sheets of rain against the sides of buildings. My camera was wet. I was wet. I headed for the Hastings police station. If any news happened that night it would come through the police station as far as I was concerned. I would keep Sergeant Frank company.

During the long night we waited. An officer reported an accident on Third Street. A farmer's windshield wipers stopped working and he banged the bumper ahead of him. Nothing serious.

Then a call came in from Highway 6 where the old highway wraps around the south side of town. The caller was frantic. "We hit a child!" he kept saying. "We hit a child! A little kid in a nightshirt. Ran right in front of the headlights. Bam! Couldn't see him 'til it was too late. We slid off the road. Can't find him. Can't find him."

"Where are you?" the Sergeant Frank asked.

"We're by, uh--there's a Debus Bakery sign."

"Which side?"

"Oh, for God's sake, hurry!" the man said. "We've looked all over, in the ditches, in the bushes, everywhere."

I could hear his voice on the phone across the room.

"Calm down," Sergeant Frank said. "Calm down. It's okay. The child has been found."

"No! You don't understand," the driver shouted back. "It just happened. It just happened--we got to a phone--you wouldn't have had time . . ."

"Look," Sergeant Frank said, "the child's been found. You're from California, aren't you?"

"Yes!" the voice said. "How did you know that?"

"Because every summer since 1938 we've had at least one call on a rainy night--it's always a carload of people from California call in from Highway 6 about where you are. You're driving east?

"Yeah."

"Your windshield wipers weren't keeping up. You couldn't see the little tyke 'til it was too late."

"Yeah."

"He turned and looked you in the face that last second."

"Yeah!"

"He had something in his hand, didn't he? Like a hobby horse?"

"Yeah! How did you know that?"

"Well, that child's been found."

"What're you talking about?"

"Back in 1938 that child was found. Dead. Ever since, people think they've seen it again. Now, you go on and have a good trip."

But they didn't.

# THE GHOSTS OF THE TEMPLE BUILDING

Carol teaches theatre at Lincoln Southeast High School. She has recently had a prize-winning production of The Insanity of Mary Girard. Several years ago, as a drama student at the University of Nebraska-Lincoln, she became one of many students who saw a ghost in Temple.

Temple Building has long been controversial. Given by the Rockefellers to provide a center for religious groups and for other purposes, the University eventually appropriated the whole thing for its secular pursuits in higher education.

In the 1940's a student died tragically in Temple Building, falling from the rigging high above the stage onto the stage itself. Preparations were underway at the time for a showing of Shakespeare's Macbeth. Since that time, according to student actors, whenever Macbeth is produced, the dead student returns.

But, in Carol's experience it wasn't Macbeth that brought back the apparition. The stage was prepared for a more contemporary play set in the 1940's. In essence, here is what Carol said.

I had gone with my boyfriend, Don, to Temple Building. He was finishing up some sets--would be working until two o'clock in the morning. Another friend of ours, Litwin, who ran the lights up in the control booth, came to do his laundry in the costume washer.

While my boyfriend worked on the set, I walked across to the old 1940's Philco cabinet radio and started twisting the dials.

Don said, "That radio doesn't work."

I said, "Just trying the dials."

Later Don went to the grand piano. Don played a little and while he was playing the radio came on.

Don said, "That can't be." We went over. It wasn't hooked up or anything, yet music came out of the speaker.

Then I turned and saw the lights had come on in the lighting control booth. I thought Litwin had come back after his washing, but some guy stood up there in the booth that I had never seen before.

When Litwin came up, we called and said, "There's somebody up in your booth. He's got the light on up there."

Litwin and his friend ran up--each taking different stairs.

As they were going up, I saw the figure in the light booth fade. He faded right in front of our eyes!

## PHANTOM IN THE TV STUDIO

The old KUON-TV studio used to be in Temple Building. A student friend of mine came to the university in the 1970's and chose a broadcasting major.

One night he was down in the east basement working on an advertising project with his TV camera. He was working late and expecting his roommate, who would stop by when he got off work. They often walked back to Harper Hall together.

At about the expected time, someone came in the front door, stopped at the landing, then came down the steps to the studio door.

My friend, Jack, said he hardly looked up from the camera until the footsteps came on into the room. That's when he looked up and saw that no one was there! The footsteps continued on across the room, but no body connected to them!

Jack said he was frozen to the camera handles--couldn't get his hands loose to run. As the footsteps crossed by in front of the camera lens, a shadowy figure of a man could be seen in the video eyepiece. Jack got his hands loose and took off running for the door. He ran all the way to Harper, more than five blocks. Later his roommate went back to Temple, shut off the camera and closed up the studio for him. Jack said he would never go back in that building again except in broad daylight and with a lot of people around.

# THE GHOST OF NEBRASKA WESLEYAN

Of all my stories, this is probably the one that has been requested the most. Every spring for several years I told it in Wesleyan's Old Main on the day that hundreds of confirmation class graduates came to tour the campus. Eight times a day I told it, until my tongue was thick, my throat sore and my brain even more rubbery than usual. Every Halloween for five years or more I told it, along with other ghost stories, for the hundreds of students and their guests who gathered either in the attic of Old Main or on the broad main stairway and halls.

I like to tell it to writing classes because of the way Chaplain Mattingly used journalistic details of who-what-when-where-how-why, and also sensory details of smell and sound as well as sight. "Notice, as you hear this story," I say to young writers, "how you know in the first few minutes exactly who is involved, where they are, and what time it is."

This story has been published in more anthologies than any ghost story I know--books such as Kettelkamp's Haunted Houses and a book Sam Dahl found called Prophecies Which Came True or some such title. (Dean Dahl was amused that this story was included in such a book because it has nothing to do with prophesy.) It was in A Guide to the Ghosts of Lincoln and more recently in a 489-page book called Haunted Heartland, by Beth Scott and Michael Norman, published in 1985 by Stanton and Lee Publishers, Inc., 44 East Mifflin Street On The Square, Madison, Wisconsin 43703.

My version of the story is not the same one I started telling shortly after the events that made it newsworthy in 1963. I interviewed Chaplain Mattingly, Dean Dahl, Coleen Buterbaugh and many others. I went through city directories, old yearbooks, and old newspapers. I also consulted The Journal of the American Society for Psychical Research. Volume 60, Number 4, October, 1966, for the article by Gardner Murphy, Ph.D., and Herbert L. Klemme, M.D., entitled, "Unfinished Business." It is the account of their clinical investigation of Coleen Buterbaugh's experience and reflections about that study.

I had been in the C. C. White Building many times through the years, but re-visited it several times before it was torn down, focusing on the rooms that figured in the story.

When all is said and done, and more said than done, I relish the events as a story. I hold it out to be nothing more. Enjoy!

Here's the story, much as I tell it.

On October 3rd, 1963, Dean Sam Dahl of Nebraska Wesleyan stepped out of his office in Old Main and said to his secretary, Coleen Buterbaugh, "Would you go over to C. C. White Building and ask Dr. McCourt to come to a faculty meeting this noon?"

Dr. Tom McCourt was a Visiting Professor of Voice from Scotland that year. He was using the band office in the northeast corner of the first floor of C. C. White.

Coleen looked at the clock in her office. Ten minutes to nine. "Yes," she said, "I'll be glad get out and walk across campus." She stood, arranged the papers on her desk, and left the letter she had been typing, rolled into her typewriter.

Later, Coleen said, "I could just as well have picked up the telephone and called over to Dr. McCourt. But it was a lovely October day, classes would be changing at nine o'clock and I would have an opportunity to see some of my friends."

So, Coleen went out the north door of Old Main, which still stands on the Wesleyan Campus. She walked northeast a hundred yards across the campus to C. C. White Building, an 1880's three-story red brick music building. It was a building soon to be condemned for demolition.

She went up the steep south steps, pulled open the heavy door and immediately heard the sound of the pipe organ playing in the great auditorium upstairs. She walked down the long wooden-floored hallway and could see, through windows in the north hall doors, the new Willard Sorority House which had been built across Madison Avenue the year before. From downstairs came the sound of band instruments being tuned for nine o'clock band practice. Next door, the girls were having a noisy Freshman Orientation.

But, as Coleen stepped into the outer office she would need to go through to get to the inner office, she noticed that all the normal sounds of the building had disappeared. She couldn't hear the practice rooms down the hall, nor the band instruments, nor the traffic on Madison. It had become deathly quiet.

As she approached the inner office door, she was struck by a strong odor of mildew. "It wasn't a little whiff," she said, "but a jolt, as if I were pushing open an old cellar door that had been closed for months."

When she pushed open the inner-office door, instead of seeing Dr. McCourt, as she had hoped to, she saw an extremely tall woman. The figure was facing away, reaching up into one of the cubbyholes where the band music was kept on the north wall.

Coleen said, "As I looked at her, I had the distinct impression that she was not alive. I don't know how I knew that, except that she was not dressed like anybody in our time. She had on a long brown satin dress, high-buttoned shoes, shirtwaist with white ruffles around the cuffs of the sleeves and around the collar, and her hair was piled up in a bouffant hairdo.

"I looked away from her," said Coleen, "looking for relief out the north window--trying to see some familiar thing. But outside everything familiar had vanished. Willard Sorority was gone. Madison Avenue was gone and in its place an old country road. Across that road was a two-story white farm house, and pasture! There was no modern thing outside that window. Then I realized that I was looking at an early-day scene of the edge of University Place (the village which was taken into Lincoln).

"I turned and fled from the room," Coleen said, "through the outer office and into the hallway. Then I heard the familiar sounds of the building again--the freshmen next door, the organ upstairs, and the band downstairs. In fact, the marimba which I had heard before was still playing. I had heard it when I had stepped in, so I knew that not much time had elapsed. Until that moment I had no idea how long I'd been in the inner office.

"However, I simply couldn't go back to face Dean Dahl," Coleen continued. "Not in the condition I was in. I went downstairs and talked with a student in the band room until I felt a little more calm. Then I walked back across the campus, into Old Main, and sat down at my typewriter again."

Mrs. Cook in the admissions office saw Coleen coming across toward Old Main. She said, "Coleen Buterbaugh looks like she has seen a ghost!"

Coleen said, "When I returned to my office in Old Main, I tried to finish the letter I had been typing when I was interrupted. I made mistakes. I would erase a mistake and then type a mistake right over the mistake. I was too distracted by what I had seen."

Dean Dahl walked out of his office and stopped at Coleen's desk. He simply stared at her for a moment.

"What's wrong?" Coleen asked. "Why are you looking at me that way?"

"You look so different, somehow," he said. "Has something happened to you?"

"Oh! I've had an awful morning," Coleen said.

Dr. Dahl sat down. "Tell me about it," he said.

"I'm afraid you'll laugh," said Coleen. "You won't believe what I think I saw."

"I won't laugh," he said. "It's too serious for that."

Coleen poured out her story, of how she had gone at Dean Dahl's request to get Dr. McCourt, of how she had found a tall woman dressed as in the long ago, and of how, even when she looked outside she stared into an early-day scene of the edge of University Place.

"How strange!" said Dean Dahl. "It's not as if that woman were in your time, but as if you had stepped through a time warp back into her time."

"That's exactly the way I felt," said Coleen.

Dr. Dahl thought a moment. "I wonder who used to occupy that northeast corner office on the main floor of C. C. White years ago? I wonder who around the campus would have been here long enough to remember?"

Then Dean Dahl got an idea. "Let's go up and ask Dr. Callen," he said. "Dr. Callen has taught social studies for many years. He'll recall."

Dr. E. Glenn Callen was a popular old teacher who had an office on the third floor of Old Main.

As Dean Dahl and Coleen Buterbaugh climbed the steps, it happened that Dr. Callen was walking down. He was a rather short man with dark glasses to protect failing eyesight. They stopped on the stairway. He was going to get his mail, he said.

"Dr. Callen," said Dean Dahl, "you're the person we want to talk to. Can you remember who used to occupy the northeast corner office of the main floor of C. C. White many years ago?"

Dr. Callen scratched his head. "The northeast corner, you say? Main floor? Yes," he said, "as a matter of fact I can remember very well because I used to be a student at Wesleyan and I worked for the lady who taught piano and theory over there. I would clean and straighten her office and put music away."

"What did she look like?" Coleen asked.

"She was a tall lady," Dr. Callen said. "Always dressed sort of old fashioned, even for her time."

"You mean," asked Coleen, "long satin dresses, high-buttoned shoes, shirtwaist with ruffles around the collar and cuffs and hair combed up into a bushy bouffant on top?"

"Yes!" said Dr. Callen. "That's Miss Mills, Miss Clara Mills. How did you know what a teacher looked like who has been gone for a generation?"

"Well," said Coleen, hesitantly, "I was over in C. C. White this morning and she was . . . she was, back."

Dr. Callen laughed. "You could not, of course, have seen Miss Mills. She died many years ago--way back in the 1940's."

Then Dr. Callen stroked his chin and looked puzzled. "As a matter of fact, she died in that end of the building. I remember now, a student was coming for her music lesson after eight in the morning and found Miss Mills had come in, set down her purse and gloves. She reached up to get the music for the hour, but clutched herself, fell across her desk and died of a heart attack. She hadn't even had time to take off her coat."

By this time, several students had gathered around on the stairway and were listening in. On hearing this, one of the students rushed off to the telephone and called the Lincoln Journal.

The Journal sent a reporter out who covered the story. I saw the story myself in the Thursday, October 31st, 1963, edition of the Lincoln Journal. There was a photograph of Miss Mills that someone had dug out of the file and the title of the article was, "Wesleyan Mystery: What Did She See? Can Unknown Dimension Recast Past and People?" (Article by Rose Sipe, page one, columns five through seven, continued, page eight, columns six through eight.) The article said, in part:

"On Oct. 3 Mrs. Coleen Buterbaugh of 1940 No. 59th, secretary to Dr. Sam Dahl, Dean of the College of Nebraska Wesleyan, walked briskly across the Wesleyan campus to the C. C. White Bldg., one of the older buildings on campus used mainly as a music hall.

"It was 8:50 a.m. as she walked down the long corridor to an office at the end of the hall. Sounds in the building, a marimba playing, the chatter of students changing classes, rang in her ears.

"She had been sent there to find Dr. Tom McCourt the visiting lecturer from Scotland.

"Entering McCourt's office, which consists of a two-room suite, she found all windows open and the room empty.

"Taking about four steps into the front room of the suite, a very strong odor of musty stale air hit her in the face, 'as if someone had turned on a gas jet and let the odor escape.'

"Mrs. Buterbaugh came to a stand-still, then, noticing a sudden quietness in the outer hall.

"'I had the strange feeling that I was not in the office alone. I looked up and just for what must have been a few seconds I saw the figure of a woman standing, with her back to me, at a cabinet in the second office. She was reaching up into one of the drawers,' Mrs. Buterbaugh recalled.

"She described the image as a very tall, slender, young black-haired woman dressed in a long-sleeved shirtwaist white blouse and a long ankle length brown skirt. She did not see her face.

"Mrs. Buterbaugh continued, 'I still felt that I was not alone. It felt the presence of a man sitting at the desk to my left, but as I turned around, there was no one there.

"'I gazed out the large window behind the desk and recall that the scenery seemed to be that of many years ago. There were no streets, the new Willard Sorority House that now stands just across the lawn was not there, nothing outside was modern.

"'By then I was frightened, so I turned and left the room.'

"Mrs. Buterbaugh returned to her office, convinced that what she saw was only her imagination and ridiculous to worry about.

"She recalled that as she tried to concentrate on her work, the experience she had just encountered persisted in her mind and she found it impossible to work.

"She had to talk to someone.

"Dr. Dahl was very serious as he listened closely to the story.

"Mrs. Buterbaugh and Dr. Dahl related the story to Dr. Glenn Callen, professor of Political Science and Sociology at Wesleyan and chairman of the Division of Social Sciences.

"Dr. Callen had been graduated from Nebraska Wesleyan (actually 1919) and had been on the faculty ever since. He knew of a woman, once a music teacher at Wesleyan, who seemed to fit the description of the woman Mrs. Buterbaugh had seen in the room at C. C. White.

"Checking further, Mrs. Buterbaugh found that the woman was a Miss Clara Mills who came to Wesleyan in 1912 as head of the Theory Dept. and instructor in piano and ear training. She had lived in University Place, before it was annexed to Lincoln, at 415 E. 16th.

. . .

"Dr. Callen recalled that Miss Mills had walked to school one morning in the spring against a very strong cold wind and a student had found her dead at her office desk about 9 a.m., the office just across the hall from where Mrs. Buterbaugh had her unusual experience.

"What was it that Mrs. Buterbaugh saw in that room?"

The article continued, reporting an interview with Dr. William Mountcastle, associate professor of philosophy and religion at Wesleyan. He had suggested keeping an open mind about the experience but stated, "'[I]t can never be verified that Miss Mills was the person Mrs. Buterbaugh saw in the room. But, it's very interesting, very interesting.'"

The article included a quotation from the 1915 Wesleyan yearbook--a quotation from beside Miss Mills' picture in that edition: "'A daughter of the gods thou art, Divinely tall, and most divinely fair.' -Pope."

The article concluded by quoting Dean Dahl and Mrs. Buterbaugh. Dean Dahl, speaking of Mrs. Buterbaugh, said, "'She's certainly convinced she saw something . . . what it is nobody knows. When she told me about her experience, she was as white as a sheet and cold chills went up and down my spine.'"

And Mrs. Buterbaugh said, "'I'm not one to imagine things, but when I close my eyes I can see her just as plain as day.'"

When I saw this article, I knew that here was no ordinary ghost story. It was a matter-of-fact sort of story, a straightforward news item, even if it was published on Halloween!

I telephoned my old friend, Chaplain L. E. Mattingly, now religion teacher at Wesleyan, and asked him if he knew what was going on.

"We don't know what is going on for sure," Mattingly said. "But we know it has been going on for over a year."

"What is that?" I asked.

He said, "Apparently students have been reporting that they have seen the figure of a woman in the northeast corner office of C. C. White. The students would leave Lucas Library late at night, walk around the corner of the building, heading for the fraternities and sororities across Madison Avenue, and they have seen a woman looking out the northeast office window. She had to be tall to be seen from the ground--those are high windows.

"No one thought too much about it at first--you know, students' stories--it could be a prank of some kind. But, now that it has happened to the dean's secretary, the whole campus is in an uproar."

Apparently the story I saw in the Lincoln Journal was picked up by a psychology professor at the University of Nebraska and mailed to the Menninger Institute of Psychiatry in Topeka, Kansas. The psychology professor knew a researcher at Menninger's was studying the paranormal. The clipping was picked up by Dr. Gardner Murphy, a research psychologist at Menninger's.

Dr. Murphy got on the telephone to Mrs. Buterbaugh as quickly as he could. "Mrs. Buterbaugh," he asked, "are you the one who had the paranormal experience this last week?"

"Oh!" she said, "It was awful. I never want to have anything like that happen again."

Dr. Murphy said, "We've been given a large research grant to study the paranormal and your case sounds interesting. We'd like to have you come down to Topeka and let us interview you."

"I couldn't get away," Coleen said. "My husband is out at the Air Base (which was still active in Lincoln at that time). He's working in a bowling alley at night. I work here at Wesleyan. I'd have to hire a babysitter for our children . . ."

"Don't worry about the cost," Dr. Murphy said. "We'll hire a babysitter. We'll fly you down to Topeka so it won't take long. We'll cover your salary--you talk to your husband tonight before you say no."

That night Coleen's husband said, "I think it would be a good idea if you'd go down to Topeka and, uh, talk to some doctors."

So, Coleen went. At Topeka they not only gave her the standard kinds of diagnostic tests such as the Rorschach Ink Blot and the Minnesota Multiphasic, but also put electrodes on her temples and wrists to make an electro-encephalogram. The encephalogram would measure delicate changes in the electrical activity of the muscles and would be an indicator of whether she believed her own story. It was a precursor of the later lie detector tests.

Coleen's report showed her to believe her own story. And, they could not divert her story from the narration of events as she had first given them.

One of the doctors put Coleen into a deep hypnotic trance, walked her back through the whole experience and found that, in a trance, she could recall additional information. She recalled having seen the shadowy figure of a man sitting at a desk in the outer office, for example, and now gave further details.

They did a sociological workup on her and found her to be a normal, healthy, outgoing sort of person. She was active in her community, she played touch football with her teenage boy, Gary, and didn't play with Ouiji Boards or try to stir up strange experiences.

The doctors were interested in the olfactory involvement--the strong smell she had experienced as she approached the inner office door. One type of mental illness has as one of it's symptoms a strong sense of a smell at the onset of the psychotic episode. But Coleen had none of the other symptoms of that mental disease. (Actually Dr. Murphy reported in the _Journal of the American Society for Psychical Research_ article, pp. 314 and 315, "because of our mutual interest in psychical phenomena, I interviewed Mrs. B. on three separate occasions for a total of approximately twelve hours--five and a half hours in the formal private interview situation and the remainder of the time in observations and interviews in the presence of other persons. Dates of the interviews were: May 13, 1964, March 12, 1965, and June 3, 1965.")

Coleen came back to work at Wesleyan. The following week, Dr. Murphy flew to Lincoln. He walked into Dean Dahl's office the next morning at eight o'clock. He wanted to interview the dean.

Afterward I talked to Dr. Dahl and he said, "I told Dr. Murphy that Coleen has worked for me for three years. She's a dependable woman and I have no reason to believe that she was telling me anything but the truth. And I can say this for certain, that she was a different woman when she came back from C. C. White than she was when she went over that morning." And, it is a sad part of the story, that she would never be the same again.

Dean Dahl and Dr. Murphy finished their visit about ten minutes to nine--the same time as the original event. Dr. Murphy had planned it that way. They walked out of the inner office, past Coleen's desk.

"Well, Coleen," said Dr. Murphy, "shall we go over and see where it happened?"

"Oh, no!" said Coleen. "Back to C. C. White? I didn't think I'd ever go back there." She paused, looked at the faces of her friends and said, "But, I suppose I'll go if you'll go with me."

The three of them walked across from Old Main to C. C. White--Coleen Buterbaugh, Dean Sam Dahl and Dr. Gardner Murphy. They went up the steep south steps and through the heavy doors. They immediately heard the sound of the organ in the great auditorium upstairs. They walked down the long wooden-floored hallway to the north end of the building. They could hear band instruments tuning up downstairs for nine o'clock band practice.

As they approached the north hallway door they could see through the little round-topped windows the new Willard Sorority across Madison Avenue.

Then, Dr. Murphy stopped because he had noticed a photograph, among a row of photographs, on the west wall of the hall. "Here," he said, "is a picture of a woman with her hair combed up into a bouffant."

"Those pictures," said Dean Dahl, "are old faculty portraits that probably should have been down years ago. They are yellowed and water-stained."

"Let's have a look," said Dr. Murphy.

Coleen rushed over. "That looks like the general outline of her," she said. "But I never did see her face. All I saw was the back of her as she reached up into those cubby holes on the north wall of the inner office."

"Here's the name," said Dr. Murphy, pointing at the bottom of the picture. "Miss Clara Urania Mills, Teacher of Piano, Theory and History of Music and Harmony, Nebraska Wesleyan University, 1912 until her death April 12, 1940."

They stepped into the outer office and Dr. Murphy said, "Let's pause a moment in this outer office to see if we can hear the sounds of the building."

They listened and could hear the practice rooms down the hall, the band instruments getting started, and even the traffic outside on Madison Avenue.

However, as they listened, the inner office door began to open by itself, slowly. Two sets of fingers appeared around the edge of the inner office door and continued to pull the door inward. Dean Dahl stepped back on Dr. Murphy's foot. Coleen shot out into the hall.

Then, Dr. McCourt stuck his head around the edge of the inner office door and said, "Welcome to the Spook House!"

"Oh!" said Dean Dahl. "That wasn't funny, McCourt! We about lost Coleen. Come back, Coleen. It was only Tom McCourt acting up."

Coleen came back down the hall but was now so tense she stayed in the outer office looking through the door.

After introductions, Gardner Murphy said, "Dr. McCourt? You seem to have a good sense of humor. Do you also believe in ghosts?"

"Of course!" McCourt said. "Scotland's full of ghosts." He told a little of the ghost traditions of Scotland, of castles and dungeons and graveyards. Then he said, "And you should hear the things I've heard about this building."

"What sort of things?" everyone wanted to know.

"Well," McCourt said, "students come around the corner of the building late at night after a jamming session in The Loft. They've seen a woman standing up in the window of this building--looking out of my office. I don't know how she gets in. I lock my office every night.

"The student who works in the radio station upstairs has heard a woman singing. He has orders not to let anyone in the building at night because the building is condemned. He'll go to the room where the voice is located, but when he opens the door the voice disappears.

"A couple of mornings ago I was over in the student union having my morning coffee. An old janitor came in and sat down with his mug of coffee and a doughnut. He looked up at me in a peculiar sort of way.

"I said, 'Good morning.'

"He simply stared at me.

"'Good morning,' I repeated.

"He stared.

"'Is anything wrong?' I asked.

"'You work in C. C. White, don't you?'

"'Yes, I do,' I said.

"He said, 'I wouldn't work there.'

"'Why is that?' I asked.

"'It's haunted,' he says.

"'How do you know it's haunted?'

"'I used to work there. I would be mopping the downstairs hallway and would hear a woman singing upstairs. I had orders that I wasn't to allow anybody in the building at night. The building is condemned to be torn down. So, I'd put down my mop in the bucket, lean the handle against the wall and go upstairs to tell the woman she had to leave. I'd go into the back of the great auditorium and there she'd be, singing on the stage over to the left by the organ.

"'I'd walk down the aisle between those rows of cast-iron seats--wooden seats with cast-iron underpinnings, you know--trying to think up what I was going to say to her. She was faculty, I could tell, by the way she was dressed--long dress and all.

"'But, I never had to tell her to leave. She'd leave right in front of me eyes, before I'd get to the stage. Kind of the way the television goes off at the end of the night: She'd shrink up to a spot, hang there for a little bit and then out she'd go. I didn't like that. I transferred to a different building. I'd quit Wesleyan before I'd work that C. C. White Building again.'"

Dr. McCourt paused.

"Coleen," said Dr. Murphy, "you're standing in the outer office looking like you're about to fly away. I know you're in a hurry to go, but, before you go, could you picture for us exactly where that woman was standing and how she was reaching up into those cubbyholes?"

"Oh, yes," said Coleen, as she looked fearfully through the doorway. "She was standing right there and reaching up into that hole! That hole right there!" She pointed.

"Do you mean to say that you can recall the exact cubby hole the woman was reaching into?" asked Dr. Murphy. "Out of all these rows of holes?"

"Oh, yes! It's frozen in my memory."

"Would you come over and show me?"

"No! This is as far as I'm coming," Coleen said.

"All right," Dr. Murphy said. "I'll reach up. Is this the one?"

"No," said Coleen. "You're too low. It's up one row."

There were rows of cubicles where the band music was kept. It was a band office McCourt was using for his choral work.

"It's that one right up there," said Coleen, pointing.

"This one?"

"Yes."

Dr. Murphy reached in and pulled out the music. Lo and behold! It was not band music! They checked every other cubbyhole and it was all band music as it should have been. But this particular cubbyhole which Coleen pointed to from the outer office had old, old choral music--some of the very music with "Clara U. Mills" stamped on it from twenty-seven years earlier.

(The "Unfinished Business" article from the Journal of the American Society for Psychical Research states: "Miss Mills, who had used this office many years before, had been concerned with choral singing . . in the upper two right-hand shelves of the music cabinet, to which the figure had been extending its right arm, was found a series of items of choral singing from Bach, from Pergolesi, and from Thomas Whitney Surette's 'Concord Choral Arrangements.'" p. 317)

This is where the story used to end. I enjoyed telling Prof. Mattingly's story for several years. But it has not ended there. Appearances have occurred since.

I was asked to tell the story one Halloween for Channel 10's Etc. program. KOLN-TV would have the cameras out in front of Old Main and have the retold story there for telecast on Halloween night . .

I thought, "What if this whole thing is a student prank? What if there was no Clara Mills? I'll have mush on my face telling this story. So, I went to the old city directories to find out what I could. I looked all through the 1940's and no Clara Mills. But, I looked in the Lincoln City Directory for 1939 and found "Mills, Clara U. instr Nebr Wesleyan Univ h. 4717 Baldwin Av. apt. 103."

I thought, "I know that address!. That's the old St. Charles Apartments across Forty-eighth Street west of Wesleyan. I guess I'd better go over and have a look at Apartment 103."

It was late afternoon the day I went. I stood for a moment looking at the glass-paneled porch on the north entrance. The old building doesn't look like it has been changed a stick since it was built in 1922. I stepped into the foyer and looked at the row of mailboxes. There was a name in every slot until I came to 103. No name.

I stood there a moment, trying to think how I would find out who lived in apartment 103, when I noticed a young woman had stopped on the stairway and was looking at me. There is a split-level hallway with a half a dozen steps.

I said, "Hi," and gave her a friendly wave.

"May I help you?" she asked. She recognized that I was a stranger here.

"I was only trying to find out who lives in 103. There's no name in the slot," I said.

"Oh," she said, "we don't have anybody in 103. They don't seem to stay very long in that apartment."

It struck me as funny, considering what I knew. In a joking sort of way, I said, "What's the matter? Do they get nervous and leave?" I smiled.

She wasn't smiling. "As a matter of fact, that's what happens. Do you know something about it?"

I laughed. "No," I said, "I was only joking. Seriously, I was just trying to find the name of somebody who lived there a long time ago."

"Perhaps I can help," she said, "I've lived here quite awhile."

"Oh, no," I laughed. "It was long before your time. It was way back in 1940 that this woman died."

"I suppose she died in that 103 apartment," said the young woman apprehensively.

"No," I answered, "as a matter of fact she died in her office at Wesleyan--she used to teach music at Wesleyan and has supposedly reappeared there."

The young woman standing on the steps clapped both hands to her mouth. She turned white. "The ghost of Nebraska Wesleyan?" she asked, as if horror-stricken. "That lady used to live here? In our apartment building?"

"Well," I said, attempting to back pedal, "the city directory seems to say that, but one can't always tell. It could be a mistake in the directory."

"Oh, no!" she said. "Oh, no!"

"What's wrong?" I asked.

The young woman said, "I've seen her. So that's who that woman is."

"What have you seen?" I asked.

"I've seen her. Jane's seen her--Jane lives across the hall."

"What have you seen?" I asked again.

"She's a great tall woman, isn't she?"

"Yes, she's supposed to be quite tall."

"She dresses in those long dresses with funny, pointed button shoes?"

"Yes."

"Has a big, Afro-like pile of hair on her head."

"Yes!"

"Oh, my gosh!" The young woman seemed to be trying to get her breath for a moment and still had both hands clapped up to her face. "Icome home from work in the winter time and it's already dark by the time I get here. I stop to look for my mail, and there she is, standing on those steps I just walked down. She has the most vivid stare. She's always staring at something back behind me. I can't help but turn around to see what she's looking at and there's nothing there. When I look at the stairway again this woman is gone."

The young woman shuddered violently as if she were taking a chill.

"Has anyone else seen her?" I asked.

"The state senator who used to live here."

"What did the senator see?" I asked.

"He came around the corner of this building one night and saw this tall woman standing right in the bush, staring at him. She didn't answer when he spoke. You can't stand where she was standing. There used to be a walk, but now we've planted bushes.

"He came into the building and told some people what he'd seen. He went up to his apartment that night and sat down in the sofa chair to watch the evening news. While he was watching TV he said he had the most peculiar feeling that somebody was behind him, watching him. He jumped up and turned around, but nobody was there. Yet, the feeling grew. He even looked in closets and other rooms because he was so sure someone was in the apartment.

"He came back, sat down and tried to finish watching the news when the television browned-out. It simply quit. He went over, switched the channels around, turned the TV off and on, plugged it into a different outlet and still it wouldn't come on. So, he switched all the dials back the way they were before and went to work on budget reports.

"He said he went to bed early that night--he couldn't watch the ten o'clock news anyway. He woke up about two o'clock in the morning with that same strong feeling that someone was in the room with him. It was so strong, he said, he had the feeling that he could reach out and touch whatever or whoever it was.

"He didn't reach out that side. He reached along the wall until he found the light switch. Switched on the light and--nobody there. He went around again and checked closets while the feeling of a presence grew.

"Then, he said, he thought of the keyhole in the hall door. He jerked open the door and jumped out into the hallway. Nobody there. Then, while he was out in the hall, the feeling of being watched left him. And, at the same moment, he heard his television come back on."

I thought, as I heard this young woman's story, "Wow! If there is this much involvement in the apartment where Miss Mills lived in 1940 when she died, I wonder where she lived in 1939 and 1938 and 1937.

The city directories indicated that Miss Mills had lived in the same apartment through most of the 1930's. Back in 1928 I found a listing: "Mills, Clara U, instr Neb. Wesleyan Univ h 100 St Charles Apts." In 1926-27: "Mills, Clara U instr Neb. Wesleyan Uni h 401 St. Charles Apts."

There didn't seem to be any problem in those apartments.

I kept searching back until I found that before 1926 she had lived for several years in a big white house only a couple blocks south of the Wesleyan campus. The day I went over I couldn't find a number on the house. Since the house was on a corner and faced two different streets, I inquired next door to see if the white house was the address I was seeking

A young woman answered the door, wiping her hands on a towel as she spoke. "May I help you?" she asked.

I showed her the slip of paper with the address. "Is this the house next door?" I asked.

"Yes, it is," she said, "but you don't want to go there!"

"Why not?" I asked.

"Because that woman is not right." The young woman pointed significantly to her head.

"Mental troubles?" I asked.

"Oh!" she said. "That woman keeps coming over and declaring that she has seen a tall woman in her upstairs hallway."

"Really?" I asked.

"We go over and help her look under beds in upstairs rooms--there's nobody there. Just yesterday she was over here and claimed that she saw this strange woman in a mirror at the end of her upstairs hallway. The woman was in old-fashioned dress and was peering over her shoulder. This neighbor of mine said she whirled around and couldn't see anybody, but every time she looked into the mirror she could see that woman again.

"Now, you know that's not right." The young woman tapped her forehead knowingly and said, "I'm afraid she's going to have to be taken away. So, please don't go over there and bother her."

I didn't go next door because I was asked not to. But I've wished ever since I would have explained to the young woman with the towel in her hands why I was there. She might have had more regard for her neighbor.

I went ahead and told the story on Channel 10. It brought quite a little response with letters and phone calls. Other people claimed to have seen Clara Mills.

A couple of music teachers in Iowa recalled their days as students at Wesleyan. They said they were walking down the long hallway in C. C. White with "Pop" Bennet, the music teacher who followed Miss Mills. He stopped and said, "Listen to the music coming from that practice room! I don't know anybody on campus who is performing that." He stepped over to the practice room, eased open the door, and--nobody in there! The music had faded away.

Another teacher in Iowa recalled that, as a student at Wesleyan, she had walked out the north hall door with a girl friend the morning of Coleen's frightening experience. They had smelled the strong musty odor. The odor was so strong that they were startled and ran all the way across the campus to Willard.

One morning, a few days after the telecast, I was walking across the campus of the University of Nebraska, where I spent twenty years, and I saw a friend of mine coming out of the communications building.

"Good morning, Foster," I said.

"Good morning, Duane," he answered. "I saw you on television the other night."

I thanked him for making reference to it.

He said, "I was the one who put the student language lab into C. C. White Building years ago."

"You were!" I responded. "Did the ghost of Wesleyan grab you?"

He chuckled and switched his cigar to the other corner of his mouth. He said, "I never heard the story of the ghost of Wesleyan until you told it the other night."

"So, there's nothing to it, right?"

"Well, I don't know," he hesitated. "I've always wanted to tell someone the things I heard in that building."

"What did you hear?"

"Everything. It was the noisiest building I was ever in, for being empty."

"It wasn't empty," I remonstrated. "It was used right up until it was torn down."

"It was empty. The whole campus was empty. I asked to put the language lab in during the Christmas vacation, so there wouldn't be students messing around with my equipment. In those days they emptied out the whole campus. I had to get a key from Administration before the beginning of the winter break.

"I'd go over each day, climb those steep south steps of C. C. White, go in and lock the door behind me. I didn't want somebody coming in and vandalizing the building while I was there. So, I'd go up to the lab, plug in my soldering iron and--'Bump, bump, bump, bump, bang.' Somebody had come down some steps somewhere nearby and banged a door.

"I'd shout down the hall: 'Hey! Who is in the building?'

"No answer.

"I'd have my soldering iron hot before long and would be about ready to sweat in a joint when--'Thump, thump, thump, thump' right down the hallway behind my back.

"I'd jump out into the hall and yell, 'Hey! Who's in here?'

"No answer.

"After several days of this, I was getting kind of jumpy. I didn't even want to go to work.

"One morning I woke up and saw that it was a howling blizzard outside. I thought, 'I don't have to go to work today! I don't want to work in that place.'

"Three days of storm. On the fourth day, I heard in the afternoon on the radio that they were opening up the streets out at Wesleyan. I drove out and parked about four blocks from the campus. I had to wade hip-deep drifts to get over to C. C. White. None of the walks were scooped.

"I kicked the snow away from that big south door, stepped inside, pulled my four-bucklers off so they could drip off on the straw mat while I was working. Looked outside and could see the streetlights were already coming on. It was getting dark early and I had taken too long to get out to Wesleyan that afternoon.

"I didn't want to work in that C. C. White Building at night, but, I thought, I'll get a few connections made and go home. I needed to get my work finished up before the students came back from vacation.

"Up in the language lab, as my soldering iron was heating, I heard that 'Bump, bump, bump, bang!' Somebody had come down a set of steps and banged a door.

"I yelled down the hall. 'Hey! Who's in the building?'

"No answer.

"I thought, 'I'll get one connection done, and then I'm going home.'

"I was melting solder into a connection when I heard it behind me. Breathing! Breathing! Slow breathing! I knew it wasn't more than a few feet behind my neck. I turned slowly to see and the only thing I could see moving was the shadow of a tree branch on the wall--a shadow cast by a streetlight outside the window.

"That did it! That was enough! I was getting out of there. I started slamming tools back into my tool chest and I made really good time going down those stairs. I grabbed up my rubber boots and stepped outside. Locked that C. C. White door behind me.

"It was so quiet outdoors you could hear a squirrel run across a tree branch a block away. You know how it is after a storm. It made me realize how noisy it was in that building.

"Then I looked down to where my tracks had broken through the snowdrifts and had turned and come up the steps. I thought, 'I'm just going to make sure.' So I walked around the building to see where any other tracks had come into the building, and my tracks were the only tracks on campus! Whoever was in that building had been in there through four days of storm--or hadn't left any tracks."

They tore down C. C. White in the summer of 1973 and when they did some of us thought that it would be the end of the story. The night before the building was to come down, I got a call from a friend of mine--Dave Hutchinson (no relation).

Dave said, "Hutch, we've got to go through the building one last time." He had made arrangements with the demolition people.

I said, "Come on, Dave! That building is ready to fall down."

"Aw," he countered, "that building is strong. They just wanted a new building so they got this one condemned."

I chuckled, as he expected. Typical student attitude toward the administration.

We went over. Dave had infrared film in his camera. Sometimes a hazy green spot will show up from a suspicious cold place. The building looked hollow-eyed with windows gone. The pipe organ was gone--everything of value removed from the building. As we walked through the hallways over broken glass and plaster, we could hear the echoes of our voices. Here and there an abandoned curtain flapped at a vacant window. I didn't like it.

Dave said, "Let's go up in the attic."

I said, "Dave! This place is ready to fall down. Let's get out of here."

"Come on," Dave urged.

We went up to the attic. I will always remember the feeling I had while creeping across that attic. I could look down through the cracks in ceiling plaster into that huge auditorium below. By the light of the moon or a streetlight shining across the stage, I could see the ragged hole where the organ console had been jerked out of the stage. Fragments of tubes and cables hung forlornly over the side of the hole. I heard a piece of plaster drop from my feet down to the auditorium floor thirty or forty feet below.

I said, "Dave! Let's get out of here before we get killed."

Dave said, "Keep your feet on the studs."

We did manage to get out without getting killed, or I wouldn't be telling this story. Dave didn't get anything on his infrared film and I didn't see or hear anything that couldn't be explained as a creaky, settling, old building.

A couple of years later I was telling stories down at St. Mary's Catholic Elementary School across from our state capitol. At the end of the session the teacher asked, "Duane, would you tell the story of the ghost of Nebraska Wesleyan?"

I whispered, "C'mon. These are fourth and fifth graders."

I once had a fifth grade girl throw up in class when I told that Wesleyan story. It turned out she had the flu, but at the time I was afraid maybe it was the story that had done it.

"It's all right," the teacher assured me. "I've told most of it to my children. I was at Wesleyan when that happened and knew Coleen Buterbaugh."

So I went ahead and told the story. At the end the teacher asked, "Did you hear what happened when they tore down C. C. White Building?"

"Nothing happened," I said firmly. I felt as if I had kept in touch with the Wesleyan campus.

She gave me a slight smile which said, "Are you sure?"

"Well, there was one thing," I recalled. "Did you know what the girls did in Johnson Hall?"

"No."

"As you know, that was the closest dorm to old C. C. White. The women became concerned as they watched C. C. White go down. Where was Miss Mills going to go, without a building to haunt? So, some of them got together and held a seance that night. They said, 'Clara Mills? Clara Mills? Come over to Johnson Hall.'

"The crazy nuts," I laughed. "I would no more do that than anything. But, they didn't get any results. They didn't feel that Miss Mills came over and joined them."

The teacher laughed at this, but then grew serious again. "Did you hear about the big two-storey white house across Madison Avenue?"

When she said that, the first thing I thought of was the two-storey white farmhouse which Coleen had reported seeing across Madison Avenue, and the pasture behind it.

"What about that house?" I asked nervously.

"That house," she said, "was owned by friends of mine. They had two high school boys who sat in the living room and watched C. C. White Building torn down. By nightfall there was nothing left but a pile of bricks and toothpicks and dust.

"During that night, the boys were terrorized by hearing someone walk down the hallway outside their room. They were afraid to come out of their room until the next morning. They ran downstairs and told their parents what had happened during the night.

"Their dad said, 'If you hear somebody else walking around upstairs tonight, you'd better stick your head out and see who's there.'

"The next night they heard it again. So, the younger of the two stuck his head out the door. He said, 'I saw it going down the hall. It was very tall and it sort of twisted back and forth as it walked. I couldn't tell whether it was a man or woman. When it turned and went past the hall window I could see that it was solid.'

"The next morning when the family got up, they found the breakfast table set European style, with the tablespoons across the top of the plate. None of them had done it.

"They became so upset with things happening in the house after that, that they put the house up for sale and sold it. The people who bought it from them only stayed in the house for six months and sold it. The people who bought it from them only slept in the house two nights and sold it. After that, no family lived there--only individual roomers."

I thought maybe this was the end of the story. But a couple of years later I was out at Eagle, Nebraska, twenty miles east of Lincoln, and a friend of mine said, "Duane, tell the story of the ghost of Wesleyan to my class."

"Bill," I said, "these are fourth and fifth graders."

"It's all right," he said. "I was at Wesleyan and knew Coleen Buterbaugh. I've told the kids most of it."

So, I went ahead and when I was a few minutes into the story I noticed a fifth grade girl about ten feet from me. Her face was twisted with fear and her complexion was turning greenish white. She had her hands pressed up around her neck. I was afraid she was going to lose it.

I stopped the story and went over to apologize to her. "I'm sorry," I said, "if this story is upsetting you. You are way out here twenty miles from where it happened. There is nothing for you to worry about. Why don't we tell another story?"

"No, Mister," she said. "I want to hear it."

The rest of the kids were all yelling, "Go for it!"

So I went ahead and told the story. The little girl stayed in that same position with her hands up to her neck and cheeks. Her color hadn't improved a bit.

At the end of the story I went over and apologized again. "I'm sorry if this upset you. There's nothing to worry . . ."

"Oh, no! Mister," she said. "I <u>wanted</u> to hear it. You see, I didn't know what you called them things."

"What things?" I asked.

"That shirtwaist and that buff thing on her head."

"You mean, the bouffant hairdo?" I asked.

"Yes."

"Why did you want to know what those things were called?"

"Because I've seen her, Mister," she said, extravagantly nodding her head.

"Come on, now!" I said. "You are twenty miles. . ."

"Oh, no, Mister. You see, I take dance lessons at the O'Donnell

Auditorium on the Wesleyan Campus every Wednesday after school. I saw her two weeks ago last Wednesday night."

"What did you see?" I asked.

I must have looked doubtful because she said, "If you don't believe me, you can talk to my mom. She was there with me."

"I believe you," I assured her, "but I would like to talk to your mom." I hoped to mend fences.

"My mom will be in the school parking lot at five after three this afternoon. She comes to pick me up."

"Please tell me," I pleaded. "What happened the day you went to dance class?"

"My mom took me to class and that day we got there early. None of the other kids were there. None of the lights were on--just the exit lights.

"So, I ran down the aisle and jumped up on the stage where we dance. It was so dark up there on stage that I couldn't find the light switches.

"I called to my mom, 'Hey, Mom? Would you go turn on the house lights?'

"Mom turned around and went back up the aisle and that was when I realized there was a big tall lady standing right by me in the dark. She hadn't said a thing.

"I said, 'Hi.'

"She didn't answer. She wasn't very friendly, I guess.

"I said, 'Hi.'

"She just stood there looking over my shoulder at something behind me.

"I screamed. 'Mom! There's a lady up here. Maybe she wants to talk to you.'

"Mom came on the double because she can tell when I'm scared. Mom jumped up on the stage just as that lady was wiping out. She just went 'Zap!' and she was gone. Mom and I looked all over up there on stage, but she wasn't anywhere.

"Anyway, Mom got an impression of her just before she disappeared, so Mom believes me."

That afternoon, about three, I went out to the parking lot. I saw mother and daughter talking at the car, waiting for me. I apologized again to the mother and explained that I didn't want to hurt anybody, the story was just for entertainment and to show how stories are written, using lots of details--and anyway it is twenty miles away.

"No," the mother said. "I'm glad you told that story. You see I was there with my daughter and I know it happened. She was so frightened after that dance class that she wouldn't go in to the next dance classes unless all the other children were with her.

"It was good you told the story," the mother went on, "because my daughter has needed some older person to talk it over with."

Later that fall, at Halloween, I told ghost stories in Old Main.

It was the fourth year in a row. Several hundred students were there, crowded onto the stairway and into the second-floor hall. I kept on, answering requests, until it was almost midnight. I was tired and wanted to go home.

After we dismissed, the kids stood around and contributed stories of their own. A couple of college men edged up to me on my right and whispered, "Wait until everybody is gone. We want to talk to you."

As soon as the others had gone, these fellows came up and one said, "You know that story about the little girl and her mother coming to dance class in O'Donnell?"

I said, "Yes."

"Well, we know it's true because we were there."

"Really?" I asked, a little alarmed. "Did you do something?"

"No. You see, my roommate here is an organ major. I'm a piano major. We were coming over to practice when the mother and daughter came racing out of that auditorium. They were coming so fast we thought the building was on fire.

"I asked, 'Shall we call 911?'

"The mother said, 'No! There's a ghost up there on stage!'

"Well! My roommate is really excited about that ghost. He wanted to see it. So he went tearing up on stage and saw it just as it was fading out. I ran up there too, but I was a little too late. I had an impression that someone was there, but I couldn't really say I saw anyone."

When I stepped out the west door of Old Main that night, I heard the bell at old First Methodist Church gonging midnight. Here I stood, at midnight on Halloween, wondering, "What has this woman, who hasn't been here since 1940, got to do with these modern buildings?"

I looked to my left past the O'Donnell Auditorium and could see over in the direction of the big house which faces on two streets--the house where the woman was thought to be going crazy because she claimed to have seen a tall woman wandering in her upstairs hallway. Then I looked the exact opposite direction and I could see the Smith-Curtis building which has replaced C. C. White. Across Madison Avenue stood the two-storey white farmhouse which Coleen had seen, against a rural setting of vacant pastures. It may also have been the same house where the boys had seen the tall twisting figure walking in their upstairs, the night after Clara Mill's building had been destroyed . .

Then I suddenly remembered that on the morning she died, Miss Clara Mills had walked across the campus against a heavy, cold, northeast April wind. That wind was thought by some to have brought about her death by heart attack minutes later. She would likely have walked through the very place where I was standing. She would have gone through the southwest corner of the O'Donnell Auditorium where she has been seen. It gave me a strange feeling.

Well, in any story of this magnitude, involving so many people and so many sightings, there are bound to be some hoaxes and pranks pulled. It is said that soon after the first ghost sighting by Coleen Buterbaugh, Chaplain Mattingly and the new coach put their heads together to play a prank. The coach was tall and thin and had a good sense of humor. So, one night, when a lot of students would be walking around the corner of C. C. White Building, the coach dressed up in a bouffant hair wig and a shirtwaist. He stood up in that corner office window with a flashlight shining under his chin.

That night several dozen students walked around the corner of the building. The coach was up there with the light illuminating his face from beneath--looking horrible. And the result? Not a single one of those students happened to look up to see him. It made the pranksters so mad that they had gone to so much trouble, for nothing!

Then, one Friday in the fall of the year, I was driving home from a storytelling trip in Iowa. I called my wife in Lincoln to say when I expected to be home. She said, "Duane, we've had a call from a Wesleyan student. They've had trouble over there, they say."

"The ghost?"

"Allegedly," she said.

I found the story that weekend. According to the tale, a freshman student from Western Nebraska collapsed on the east lawn of Old Main. The Pinkerton nightwatchman found him and called an ambulance. By the time the ambulance arrived, the boy was awake, but became hysterical when they tried to get him into Old Main. "Not in that building," he wailed.

They helped him into the new library and set him down in an easy chair. Students crowded around while he gradually got out his story. He was walking on the east side of Old Main, he said, when he looked up and saw Old Main looking like a new building! The vines were gone. The structure looked freshly built, but it was Old Main all right. Then he said he saw the face of a woman looking at him from an upstairs window. The same face appeared next in a first storey window, close by the student. That was the last thing he could remember. He must have fainted then.

Had he heard of the ghost of Wesleyan? The students crowding around wanted to know. No, he hadn't heard of that.

Then a librarian quietly walked over to a bookshelf and pulled out a 1915 Coyote (the early-day name for the Wesleyan student annual). The librarian turned the pages until she came to the page with the photograph of Miss Clara mills, along with other pictures of women faculty. The librarian edged through the crowd of students and held the open book in front of the freshman.

The boy asked, "What's the book for? Ahhhhh!" he screamed, "there she is! That's her!" And he pointed at the face of Clara Mills!

It makes quite a story anyway.

But, a curious thing about the many "sightings" of Clara Mills is that the woman who is seen is always the woman as she appeared in the 1912-1915 period, never Miss Mills as she was at the time of her death in 1940. In the early years she had the look of a beautiful, but troubled musician. In later years she had a more calm, less severe look. Her hair was no longer in a bouffant, piled up on top, but more combed down. She had a kindly, matronly look, as of someone a person might go to for counsel. This woman of older years is never seen.

Perhaps we are not dealing with a ghost at all, but a strong psychological impression left by a frustrated young artist?

## THANK YOU FOR WHAT YOU'VE DONE

One lovely October, I spoke in a small high school and told some ghost stories. Afterward I was led into a side room for a conference with the math teacher. He had something he wanted to share and here is his story:

My religious group which holds weekly sacramental meetings.

Last week I was up at Norfolk attending one of the meetings. In that group is a fine man, George Grey, one of the most respected men of the community. George has had an interest in young people for a long time. He even "adopted" a teenage boy whose parents had been killed in a car accident on Highway 275.

George spoke in the meeting of an unusual experience during the week. He said to the group, "As you know, Larry came to live with us two years ago." He nodded to Larry who was a new member of the group. "And, as you know, Larry has had some troubles since his parents died. He has had some run-ins with drugs and so on. It was pretty hard for all of us for awhile there, wasn't it, Larry?"

Larry smiled. His troubles were well known to Norfolk people.

"But now this is past," George went on, "and Larry is turning out to be a fine young man.

"Well, this last Monday I was home in the afternoon. I stepped out on the back porch and looked off across the yard. As you know, this has been a glorious fall. Our marigolds have been doing better than they did all summer.

"I stepped off the back porch, walked out in the yard and was suddenly aware that somebody was behind me--between me and the house. I turned around and looked, and here was a lady, all nicely dressed up, standing on the back step where I had just been!

"I walked toward her and introduced myself, asking what I could do for her, and she simply smiled and said, 'Thank you for what you have done for Larry.' Then she faded away."

George said, "I swallowed a couple of times, and ran around to the other door to get into the house to call Larry at the lumber yard. I told Larry what had happened. He asked me a lot of questions. I told him what she was wearing, nearly as I could remember."

"That was Mom!" Larry said, "She wore that dress day she died."

We all turned and looked at Larry and he said it was all true. "That was the way it was," he said.

# THE RANCHHOUSE GHOST

A friend of mine, a professor at the University, told me this one about his grandfather's ranch in north central Nebraska.

My grandfather bought a ranch that had been homesteaded by a Dutch family. There was tragedy in the background of the ranch. The old widow lived in the ranchhouse for many years with her alcoholic son. The fellow was in his thirties and did little work. He'd run off to town on two or three-day binges and leave his old mother out there to fend for herself.

The ranch was running down. The mother was getting feeble. The boy didn't take care of her like he should. When she became bedfast and the neighbors knew the boy had left, some of them went over to investigate.

The neighbors found the woman in the cellar. She had gotten thirsty and crawled all the way from the upstairs bedroom to the cellar and was trying to get water out of the rainbarrel.

The poor old soul only lived a short time after the neighbors found her. The last thing she said, over and over, was, "I'm going to get even with that son of mine."

Two weeks later the son was found dead. He had mashed his head to pulp on the top of a fence post.

Was it homicide? Suicide?

When Grandfather bought the place he had a scare one night. He slept over on the side of the house next to the horse barn. He liked to keep track of his horses.

One night there was a terrible commotion in the barn. Sounded like the horses were kicking out the sides of the barn.

Granddad jumped up and saw a figure, a white-light figure in the shape of a man, standing in front of the barn door.

Granddad took his shotgun out and challenged the man--if that's what you could call a figure made of light. It was simply the shape of a man, made out of glowing radiance.

"Come forth!" Granddad said.
The figure didn't move.
"Who are you?" Granddad called.
The man in white stood his ground.
"Speak or I'll shoot."
No move.
Granddad shot in the air.
Still no move.
Granddad fired at the figure until he was out of shells.
When Granddad picked up a brick to throw and couldn't get it out of his hand, Granddad retreated.
The next day there was a pattern of buckshot on the side of the barn, outlining the figure of a man.

In later years, continued the professor, my grandfather had a hired man who was a powerful, muscular fellow. One time when a wheel came off a wagonload of earcorn, the hired man crawled under the wagonload and lifted the axle until the wheel could be put back on.

One night this hired man was heard swearing in his bedroom. He was shouting and carrying on so, Granddad went to the man's room to see what was wrong.

The hired man swore some more and said, "Somebody's been pulling down the covers."

"You've been having a nightmare."

"'Taint a nightmare, I tell you. Somebody's pulling down the covers."

Granddad went back to bed. A short time later Granddad heard the hired man swearing again.

Granddad went down the hall and this time he could see it--something was pulling down on the covers so hard that the hired man's hands ripped the covers pulling against the force.

The neighbor down the road, when she heard it, said, "Oh, that's Granny Van Loon all right. She'd always roll the covers down and hang the roll halfway out the window to air on nice days."

By the end of his life, Granddad had built so many additions around the sides of his original ranchhouse that the room in the center had no outside wall. Granddad liked to go in there to read by candlelight because no breeze would bother him there.

But, one night, somebody went, "Poof!" and blew out his candle flame.

Granddad got up and accused his boys of blowing out his candle. But none of the boys was close. They said they didn't do it.

Granddad relit his candle and went back to reading. In a little bit, "Poof!" Out went the candle.

Granddad got up and stamped around, accusing everybody. "If it happens again," he said, "there's going to be trouble."

The third time the candle blew out, Granddad lost his temper completely. He destroyed the room, slamming his chair around.

The last thing about Granddad's ranch was the visit of a gypsy caravan. The lead wagon with the gypsy queen got stuck in a mudhole out front. Granddad went out and pulled the wagon through with his team of horses.

The gypsy queen spent the time in the house while the rescue work was going on. In gratitude, she said, she would teach Grandma how to read palms. Grandma didn't have much interest in that, but as a way of being hospitable she learned how.

For years afterward, Grandma read palms and sometimes astonished people with the accuracy of her readings.

## MEADOW LANE

Several years ago I was telling stories at Meadow Lane School in Lincoln. The last day there I spent an hour, on request, telling ghost stories. During the last story, near the end of the hour, I noticed a middle-aged teacher watching me with what I took to be a severe expression. In fact, my feeling of her disapproval grew so strong it was hard to keep my mind on that last story.

After the hour, the dignified-looking teacher came to me and said, "Mr. Hutchinson. May I see you in my office?"

"Oh, oh!" I thought. "I'm in trouble." My old memories of being called to the principal's office came back.

In the office I sat meekly on the opposite side of the desk from her and was about to say, "Look, I won't do it again, whatever it was," when she spoke. Her words came slowly, cautiously, as she peered at me over the top of horn-rimmed glasses.

"Mr. Hutchinson," she said, "we had something in our house we couldn't explain. We haven't told anyone outside our family and the other family that was involved."

I felt my anxiety drain out of me.

"It is the home where we used to live," she said. "We have never told anyone--no one, that is, except the other family involved. If you would be interested . . ?"

"Would I! Please tell me," I said. Not only was I off the hook but was being offered a reward.

This is what she told:

My husband and I collect antiques. Several years ago we purchased a beautiful "antique" house, a Victorian home in the College View area. My husband would be close to his work at the fire station on South 48th and I would be close to school.

Not long after we moved in we discovered our dog, Geezer, was aware of something in the house. He'd growl and stare at what he thought was moving around the room--something we couldn't see.

You won't believe this, but one night we had the veterinarian out at our house at eleven o'clock at night, having the dog's stomach pumped. Geezer had danced along on his hind legs as if he were begging food from someone. He'd catch an imaginary scrap in his mouth, beg for more and--act as if he were eating.

The vet couldn't find anything in the stomach. He spoke of one kind of nervous stomach--a disorder that makes a dog appear to eat. But our dog had none of the other symptoms.

Shortly after this, one night, we heard our girls scream in their room across the hall. Before we could get up they were at our door, knocking and asking if they could come in and sleep with us.

We asked them what was wrong and they said somebody was in their room.

Of course, we went into their room immediately, but no one was there. We looked under beds, in closets and out the windows. As we were talking we heard the furnace come on. It was an old coal furnace that had been converted to gas. When it came on and the heat came through the pipes the house would click and creak.

We told the girls they were hearing the furnace and we managed to get them to go back to sleep.

The next week it was the same thing. The girls came in and wanted to sleep with us. We told them they would have to sleep upstairs if they didn't like the downstairs room.

"Oh, no!" they said. They didn't want to be any farther away from us than they were. "We're scared upstairs too," they said.

Another time when it happened, the girls came to our door. We were trying to get the girls calmed down and Jerry pushed them a little bit. "What do you think you see?" he asked.

"Well," Sarah said, "there's a boy in our room."

Jerry went tearing into their room. I followed. Nobody there.

Jerry said, "Sarah, what are you talking about?"

Sarah said, "He's about fifteen years old and he stands between our twin beds. He isn't looking at us or anything. He just stands there, and then he, well, he sort of fades away."

I looked at Jerry and Jerry looked at me. We wondered what was happening to our girls.

Then, one morning I went out to the kitchen and found our antique spice cabinet had all the drawers pulled out. This is a cabinet which sits on the counter and has fifteen little drawers--seven down each side and one long drawer across the bottom.

The drawers don't have stops on them, so if they're pulled too far they come clattering down to the counter and spill the spice. This morning they were pulled to the point where another slight movement and they'd fall. Even when I pushed one drawer in, the rest fell out.

Morning after morning it was that way. All the drawers were pulled out to the critical point. My husband would come out and fiddle with those drawers, but he could never get them to the exact point where a push on one would make all the rest fall out.

Then, a little game with light switches started.

I would go into the bedroom to get something and the dining room light would go off. I'd go back to see who flicked the switch and the bedroom light would go off. I'd go back to the bedroom and then the hall light would click off. It was as if someone were only a room away, playing with the switches.

My husband laughed at me--said I was simply getting nervous about the way the dog was acting, about our girls, and about those spice cabinet drawers. He laughed, until one night it happened to him.

I always left the porch light on for him because he would get home late from the fire station. We had one of those double-button light switches on the porch. If you punched in the white button the light came on and the black button popped out. Punch the black button and the light went off and the other button popped out.

One night Jerry came home, as usual, punched the porch light off, and stepped into the dining room. The porch light snapped back on. He thought he hadn't punched it hard enough so he went back out and punched it harder. Then the dining room light switched off. Then the kitchen light came on.

Jerry grumbled around there about changing the light switches. Next morning, instead of sleeping in as he was supposed to do, he bounced up early. He went to a hardware store and bought electric switches. He replaced the porch switch, the dining room switch, and the kitchen switch. But it still didn't solve the problem entirely. We still had lights going on and off.

We grew more and more tense about the whole thing. We couldn't talk to anybody about it. We were afraid they would simply laugh at us.

I developed the habit of taking Geezer with me any place in the house I went. The dog seemed to sense when something was going to happen before it happened. The laundry room in the basement was one place where Geezer seemed especially alert to the unseen.

One night I was in the bathtub, having a hot steamy bath. I love hot baths. I'll crawl in with a magazine, let a little hot water dribble in--enough to keep the water warm--and read my magazine and soak.

Geezer was on the bathmat, curled up asleep. The girls were in their room, doing homework. Jerry was at work.

I was absorbed in my magazine when Geezer started out of his sleep. He stood and growled. It was an unearthly growl, not the usual sort that a dog would growl at another dog. He stood with the hair up on his back all the way down his tail.

I jumped up and put a wrapper around me. I had felt sort of secure because the bathroom door was locked. But not now. Then the door crashed open against the wall. A rush of cold air came in and Geezer went out of his mind.

I rushed out the bathroom door into the hall and called, "Jerry? Jerry?"

The girls answered from the other end of the house and said, "Mother! You know Daddy's at work."

Nothing was outside the door!

The Meadow Lane schoolteacher told me these events with such conviction that I felt a shiver go down my back.

"You spoke," I said, "of the dog acting strange, of drawers being pulled out, of lights going on and off, and of your girls hearing, and supposedly seeing, someone. Have you, yourself, ever seen . . it?"

The teacher looked at me with such a serious expression that I grew uncomfortable.

"I'm sorry if I said the wrong thing," I said. "Forget I asked that."

"No, no." She said. "It's all right. I was only wondering what you would think if I told you."

Through her stare she seemed to be trying to gauge my ability to comprehend.

"I think you are very serious," I said.

"Well," she said, "you seem to be very understanding, so I will tell you. I need to tell somebody."

This is what she went on to say:

One night I was in bed, reading. The girls were already asleep. Jerry was at the fire station, as usual. I thought I would try to stay up until he got home, but the magazine kept falling out of my hand.

I reached up to turn the light off and saw what looked like a column of smoke in front of our bookcase. I could imagine that a fire had started in the basement and the smoke was coming up through the register. We are so fire conscious because of Jerry's work.

But, as I looked more carefully I could see it was not a column of smoke. A figure was taking shape!

He <u>was</u> a boy about fifteen or sixteen, the way our girls had said. He seemed to be looking off toward something behind me--somewhere above my head.

I sat up in bed and tucked the covers under my chin. "What do you want?" I asked him. My voice would hardly work.

He simply smiled . . . and faded!

First I saw something red in the middle of his chest. For a moment I didn't know what it was, then I saw it was our big red book of antique collectables. It was standing on the shelf behind him, about where his chest was. He seemed to fade from the center out. The last I saw of him were the tips of his fingers.

After that, I . . . I wasn't afraid any more. I felt as if I knew whom I was dealing with. Afterward I knew when he was around. It's sort of like biofeedback. When I connected a certain feeling with what I had seen, I knew when he was there. And, I knew who was there.

Sometimes I would sense his presence in the kitchen, sometimes in the dining room. Most frequently, however, he was in the basement. When I was doing laundry I could tell he was nearby.

Sometimes I would talk to him. I'd say, "Hello Jimmy." I called him Jimmy, I don't know why. I say 'I talked' to him. It wasn't a talking aloud, the way I am doing now with you. It was a kind of inner projecting of a thought. Do you know what I mean?

Sometimes I'd get the feeling he was answering me.

I suppose you think I'm crazy.

"I think you're very serious," I said.

It was sort of comforting having Jimmy around. And when my husband bought another house I was upset.

We had seen another house for sale just down the street. It was beautiful, and a good price, and it had a workshop in it which Jerry wanted.

We had talked about it. We'd agreed we liked it, but still, I wasn't prepared when Jerry came home one day and threw a sheet of paper on the table for me to see.

I looked, and it was a purchase agreement he had signed.

I said, "Jerry! What have you done?"

"Agreed to buy the house," he said.

"We can't afford it," I said.

"Look at the price," he said. "They dropped the price ten thousand dollars."

"Where are we going to get the money?" I asked.

"Sell this house."

I couldn't look at Jerry for a moment. I had the strangest feeling that I didn't want to leave this house. But, I knew it meant that we had to sell the house we were in to finance the next one.

Fortunately, some friends of ours, Ginger and--I'm not supposed to tell you their names--let's say, Jack, wanted our house. We often got together to play pinochle and now we could get together easier.

Jerry and I debated whether we should even say anything to them about "Jimmy" and his little tricks.

Jerry said, "They'd just think we're wacko if we told them. They probably won't notice anything and we don't want to spoil the house for them. If anything goes wrong, we'll give their money back."

And I did think sometimes it was all in my head.

The day we moved, we had everything on the truck, I was finishing up in the basement with the vacuum sweeper and I felt Jimmy was there. I told him he could come with us. He couldn't come. I told him goodbye.

When I came upstairs Jerry could tell I had been crying. He said, "You've been saying goodbye, haven't you?"

I said, "Yes, I have."

Jerry didn't laugh at me any more.

Three months after we were moved and Ginger and her family had settled in our old house, everybody seemed to be getting along fine. Ginger was having a great fun, getting new curtains and fitting out the house, decorating the kitchen in canary yellow and all.

Then, one morning in July, Jerry was working out in his beloved shop. The back door of the shop crashed open and there stood Jack. He was white as a laundry bag. He had come down the alley and was completely upset.

Jerry asked him what was wrong.

Jack said, "I think I'm losing my mind is all." He picked up a hammer and laid it down. "You really like your shop, don't you?"

Jerry said that he did.

Jack walked around the shop and looked at this and that. He picked a wrench off the wall hook and laid it down.

"You know we like our house," Jack said. "Ginger has had a wonderful time redecorating and getting it just the way she wants."

Then he changed the subject and talked about tools and this and that.

When he got ready to leave Jerry asked him again what was wrong and Jack suggested we get together and have supper.

Jerry invited them over to our place but Jack said we should come there.

Saturday night at supper we talked about everything except what we had come to talk about. It was really funny the way we both avoided it.

The girls excused themselves and left the table. It was nice that Ginger's girls and our girls were the same age.

The men went off to the the side of the room.

Then, at last, Ginger broke the ice. She said, "You know we love this house. But it's the first house we've ever lived in where we can't get our girls to sleep in their own bedroom."

So that was it. Same thing.

"They think there's a boy in their room," I said.

"No," Ginger said, "a girl."

I said, stubbornly, "It's a boy, about fifteen or sixteen years old."

Ginger said, "No! It's a girl--college age, I'd say."

We argued and compared notes. The girls came back from the other room when they heard us. The more we talked, the more we discovered that the presence their girls felt in the bedroom was not a boy but a girl--a young woman of college age.

Before long the men started talking about lights going on and off and they decided it must be the wiring in the attic. They discovered that neither of them had ever been up in the attic. They wondered about insulation.

Before long the men were determined to go up that very night. We knew where the attic door was and why none of us had gone up to the attic. It was in the ceiling of an upstairs closet and very awkward to get to. The little square door had even been papered over, but you could still see the square impression in the paper where the door was.

We went upstairs and realized we'd need a knife to cut the paper. Jack went down and brought a butcher knife from the kitchen drawer. Then he realized he'd need a stepladder to get up through the hole. So, the men went down to get the ladder.

The men crawled up and I could hear them talking way back in far corners of the house. Yes, the wiring was old and, yes, the house did need insulation.

Then Jerry called and said, "Hey Jack, there's a box over here."

In a moment Jack was over the attic doorway handing down that old box. It was so big it barely came through the hole.

When we opened it, the dust swirled up and stung our nostrils. We found it was full of a girl's things. There were college notebooks, underwear, a monogrammed sweater--simply the personal things of a college girl.

We knew who the family was from the girl's name in the notebooks and we recalled having seen that name in the abstract of title for the house. Ginger said she thought that family had moved to Kansas City.

We were all in such a mood by this time we called Kansas City, long distance information. We talked to the college girl's family that night.

Ginger wanted me to talk since we had owned the house first.

"Did you know there's a box of your daughter's things in our attic?" I asked.

"Yes," the mother said. Her voice sounded dull and depressed.

"Would you like us to send Millie's box to you?"

"No." That same, dull, depressed voice.

I didn't know what to say. There was a pause and the mother said, "If the box is in your way why don't you give it to The Salvation Army."

I said, "No! We're not going to give your daughter's personal things away like that. Don't you want them?"

Then she said, "I guess we just couldn't deal with it after Millie was killed. She was in that car accident while she was at Wesleyan. We got rid of most of her things, but there was one box we simply couldn't deal with. That's why we left her things in the attic. We'll come and get them some time."

But, they never have. That box is still in Ginger's attic.

Ginger and I became interested in the history of the house after this. We went down to the library and looked up city directories until we found out everybody who had lived in the house.

We found there had been a sixteen-year-old boy who had been killed in our basement--a James Belden. He had had a gun collection which was once featured in a newspaper story.

He had a shop in the basement. One day he was cleaning a gun while it was clamped in a vise. It accidentally discharged and killed him instantly.

When I saw his picture in the newspaper with the story of that event, I recognized him instantly.

I said, "Ginger, look at that picture."

She said, "What about it?"

Then I realized--of course she wouldn't recognize him. She had never seen him.

I said, "Ginger, there is the boy who stood in front of our bookcase that night! No question about it."

# THE GHOST OF MONTECELLI

One of the most delightful of the many who contributed ghost stories to me was an athletic man, prominent in state government. He begged me not to tell the origin of his stories. He had a respected position and was head of his department. But he leaned back in his walnut office chair, folded his arms across his great chest and told me the following:

We live in south Lincoln in a moderate two-storey house. We have a ghost. No question about it. If you sleep in our east bedroom upstairs you will hear knocking that sounds like a steel ball bouncing to rest on a hardwood table. Everyone who sleeps in the room hears it. The sound comes not from the floor, not from the wall, not the ceiling. The sound will originate in empty space about two feet to the right of the bed--in the air. You can crawl out of bed and walk around the sound.

Here. Listen to this.

He took a ping pong ball out of his desk. He dropped it on his desk top and let it bounce until it jiggled to a nervous stop.

There, like that, he said. Only it is a hard sound, like a steel ball on oak.

We have never been able to find an explanation for the ball bouncing, but the cry of a baby which follows is a different story. We have a possible explanation.

It's the anguished cry of a baby in the attic. The cry is a chilling sound, especially when you know there's no one in the attic. It's the sort of cry to galvanize you into action. You know that baby needs help and quick. But, at last, the cry dies away.

We did a little searching at the historical society and found the house was occupied by three families during World War II. A lot of families crowded into houses during the busy war years. The Air Base was here then--a lot going on, but no houses being built.

Then one day a woman came to our door. She was in Lincoln for a four-day conference, she said, and was curious to visit the house where she had lived as a child. Of course, we invited her in and showed her the house.

She said that one family occupied the whole downstairs, but her family shared the upstairs with another family. The other family also used the attic.

As we became better acquainted with this woman and shared her excitement about the house, we invited her to stay with us. She could cut down the cost of her conference. She was delighted and so were we.

We put her in the bedroom where the bouncing ball has been heard followed by the cry of the baby. The next morning after breakfast we asked her how she enjoyed her sleep.

She said, "I slept well, so happy to be back in the room where I slept as a child. But," she added, "the memory of that other family upstairs came back. Part of them slept in the attic room. And I'll never forget the night their baby died of pneumonia. I thought last night I heard again the anguished cry of that baby in the attic."

You're welcome to stay overnight in our noisy bedroom. I can promise you, you'll hear the ball bouncing. Everyone hears that who sleeps there. You may hear the baby's cry. You may not. Some do, some don't.

The government officer unfolded his hands, leaned forward across his desk and looked at me intently. If you are collecting ghost stories, he said, you should hear the one that happened to my mother.

Sure, I said. Shoot.

This won't be a Nebraska ghost story, he said. It happened over in Italy.

That's okay, I said. It happened to a Nebraskan.

This is what he told me:

My mother went to Europe with a rich girlfriend of hers in the summer of 1922. Mother couldn't afford such a trip on her own, but her friend wanted company. She said, "You go with me and I'll pay the way."

They had a great summer. They saw England, Scotland and Ireland. Took a ship to the fjords of Norway. By the end of the summer they were touring the Alps and Mother's friend didn't want to leave.

Mother had to come back to the U. S. A. She couldn't afford to stay through the winter and, anyway, wanted to get back to school. So, Mother came on home and her friend continued hiking in Switzerland.

By winter, Mother's friend was hiking on the warmer, southern side of the Alps, in Italy.

One day she had a short hike of ten kilometers or so from one youth hostel to another, but it was over a mountain pass. She was overtaken by a bad snowstorm. As she slogged along nearing the

Montecelli Mansion Hostel, the storm grew so thick she could hardly see the edges of the trail. She didn't want to fall into a gulley.

Then through the storm came an Italian Catholic priest. He was hurrying along, passing her up, oblivious of her. He was an older man with shaggy brows. Seemed not affected by the storm at all.

She called a friendly, "Hello!" but he glided past her. He wasn't friendly--unusual for a priest. She called again as he went on ahead. Still no answer. But, she thought, he seems to know where he's going, I'll follow him so I don't get lost.

It took all she had to keep up. He would appear and disappear through waves of snow. At last he turned toward a huge shadowy building looming out of the blizzard. Then she recognized it. It was the old stone Montecelli mansion. She recognized it from the Youth Hostel Handbook. It was a lovely Romanesque castle-like affair, over a hundred and fifty years old. Turrets rose above the roofline. A lot of steps went up to a huge arched doorway.

As the old priest mounted the steps of the hostel, she saw he had no snow on him like the other hikers she had seen.

The priest went up the steps ahead of her and disappeared into the mansion.

Mother's friend went on in, checked in for the night and gave little more thought to the priest. Little more, that is, until supper.

At supper all the hostellers ate in a common room in the basement. Mother's friend noticed that the old priest hadn't shown up for supper. She wondered if he was ill in his room so she went to the hostelry office and reported the clergyman was not at supper.

"There's no priest here," the desk clerk said.

"Yes, there is," she said. "I saw him come in ahead of me."

"There's no priest here."

"Look," she said, "I saw him."

"What did he look like?"

"Well," she said, "I did notice that his clergy clothes were not modern. They were the old kind like priests wore a hundred years ago."

The desk clerk's face turned white.

"What's the matter?" she asked.

"I'll call the manager."

The desk clerk continued to stare at her as the manager came out. The manager asked many questions--questions which showed he knew what she had seen.

"What's this all about?" she asked. "Is the priest a criminal or something?"

"You may have seen the ghost of Father Montecelli," the manager said.

"The what?"

"The ghost," said the desk clerk.

"You see," said the manager, "here is a booklet about the Montecelli family. There was a crime years ago. Here, this tells something of the traditions."

By this time, my mother's friend was really excited. "A real ghost. A European ghost!"

The more she learned the more excited she became. The manager told of a room up on the third floor of the hostel which had been the priest's room. No one had been able to stay in the room for years. The outside window was boarded up.

"Is there furniture in there?"

"Oh, yes," the manager said. "But it's covered with years of dust."

"I'll pay to have it cleaned," she said.

"Why?" asked the manager.

"I want to stay there."

"Oh, no. You wouldn't want to stay in that room."

"Oh, yes I would. I would. A real European ghost. Please let me stay there. I'll pay double for the room. I'll pay to have it cleaned up. Then you'll have a nice room again."

The manager said they would like to have the room cleaned up. It didn't even have electricity in it--something about the workers quitting on the job. They didn't know if it was a firetrap in there or what.

She begged more, offering to pay for restoration, and the manager mumbled something about "crazy Americans" and said he would talk to her in the morning.

The next day she found out more about the story. The Montecelli family, it seems, had been a very prominent family a hundred years before, but had been reduced to shame. A savage murder had been blamed on them. The Montecelli family members still had descendents in the area. Of the original family who had lived in the mansion, some had been imprisoned. The last remaining member of the family to live in the mansion was the old priest. He had spent his last years trying to solve the mystery of the murder and clear the Montecelli name. He had died in the room on the third floor in 1864.

The Montecelli Mansion had stood empty for forty years. It was used as a hospital and a home for the aged. It stood vacant more years and eventually became a youth hostel.

"Please let me stay," my mother's friend continued to ask.

The next day she saw the boards had been taken off the third floor window. Drapes were being aired and beaten on clotheslines behind the hostel. She peeked into the room where workers were cleaning and saw it was, indeed, a beautiful apartment. The hundred-year-old furniture remained.

She came back one afternoon following a hike and learned that the workers had quit. They refused work in a place that was haunted, they said.

The manager said, "Listen! It won't cost you a thing. Just agree that you won't ask anymore to stay in that room."

She said, "Nothing doing. You made a contract and I'm holding you to it."

"The room isn't done."

"Hire some more workers."

They did get a different cleanup crew and at last, one evening, the manager announced that the room was ready. "However, as I said before, it won't cost you a thing, if you'll forget the whole thing. Please do not stay in it. We'll not collect on your kind offer."

"You promised," she said.

"Those who cleaned don't like the room. Something is wrong. Something is present in the room we don't understand. But, we're glad the room has been cleaned. We should have done it long ago. We are leaving the boards off the window."

"We made an agreement," my mother's friend said. "Are you backing out of the agreement?"

"No," said the manager. "We are only asking you to give up the idea. There is no cost to you."

"I want to stay. I'll have something to write home about."

"All right. But, you must sign this release form. We are not responsible for what happens to you."

She signed the form and stayed.

Some of the hostellers tried to talk her out of doing it. No one offered to stay with her. She went up, alone, to the room. It was about ten o'clock. Lights' out.

The room had plastered applique on the ceiling. Marble statues stood on pedestals. A tall cherry cabinet covered one wall. The window had velvet drapes. Iron candleholders mounted on the walls and an absence of light fixtures of any kind reminded her that the room had never been wired for electricity. A cold fireplace in the corner had a bronze plate over the firebox. The bed itself was cherry with tall posts at each corner.

I know all this because I've read the letters to my mother many times.

The posts looked as if they had once held a canopy, but that had probably rotted off and been taken down.

She climbed into bed and pulled the covers around her. The tall drapes at the window were moving slightly, but that was because of a breeze around the edges of the window.

By midnight she was still awake, the covers pulled up around her, still. Light came in from the streetlamps. By one o'clock she was sleepy and very disappointed. After all this trouble, she wasn't going to get to see a ghost.

She dozed off.

When she heard the church clocktower gonging two o'clock, she awakened. Someone was in the room. She sat up in bed against the headboard. Pulled the covers up around her chin. For the first time she wished she hadn't gone through with it.

Then he appeared. The priest--the same priest who had passed her on the road--appeared as if he had materialized out of a bedpost. It was the priest with the old-fashioned garb!

As she sat up, shivering, she saw that he was looking directly at her. She spoke, as soon as she found her voice. "What do you want?"

As if in answer, the old priest slowly turned and walked toward the door. He lifted one hand and motioned for her to follow.

She jumped out of bed, threw on a coat, and followed the figure like one in a trance.

The priest walked to the end of the hall and descended a circular stone stairway. She crept along behind him, down to second, down to first, which was the basement. No one in the youth hostel would know where she had gone. She found herself asking why she was following, but continued to do so.

The old man walked across the basement room. The room was dimly lit from streetlamps reflecting on the snow outside. He approached a wall cabinet similar to the one in the room she had just left. He pointed to a particular drawer.

She grasped the drawer and pulled it open. The drawer was empty.

"It's empty," she said.

The priest continued to point to the drawer.

She pulled the drawer farther until it dropped to the stone floor. As it a clattered onto the stone floor, the drawer broke. The bottom came loose. It was a false bottom! Loose papers and envelopes slid sideways from the split drawer.

She turned to look at the priest and saw him fading, fading with a faint smile as he went.

She grasped the papers, held them to her bosom and ran back up the stairway, all the way to her room. She stopped at the door, rethought her position and ran back down to wake the desk clerk.

As she pushed the papers across the desk to the clerk, she saw the name Montecelli appearing again and again in the quaint Italian script.

The manager called the police who came and shone their flash-lights around her room and in the first floor cabinets. They took the papers and said, "We'll call you in the morning. Please stay here."

My mother's friend said that in spite of offers from other youth hostellers to stay with them, she slept in the room--and slept with a great sense of peace. Perhaps she was simply exhausted.

The next day the police came and, in a most courteous way, in-vited her to come to the station.

The police station was filled with many people. She met members of the Montecelli family who stood around a large table in the police headquarters room.

"Do you understand what these papers are?" asked the police officer.

"No, but I see the name Montecelli written in many places," she answered.

"You have found the papers," the officer said, "which we believe will prove the innocence of the Montecelli family."

There, in the Nebraska government office where my friend had told this story, all was silent for a moment. I could hear the traffic in the street outside. My friend still leaned forward on his elbows, his palms now flat on the desk top.

"My mother," he said. "still has the packet of letters from Italy--letters that her old girlfriend of the European days had given her shortly before she died. Every letter is a thank you from a different member of the Montecelli family--a thank you for having helped set their family free from a hundred years of shame.

## GHOST SIGHTERS AT SUPPER

After collecting ghost stories for several years, I noticed that people who have had a vivid experience of a ghost frequently have other paranormal abilities. In fact, I am beginning to suspect that perhaps one in every twenty-five persons has a kind of spiritual antenna that the rest of us don't have. They sidle up to you after a meeting where you've told ghost stories and say, often with apparent shyness, "Could I talk to you alone? There is something we've never told outside our family. . ."

Some of my best ghost stories have come from people who are reluctant to tell a personal experience of a ghostly nature. They often feel lonely, these people, sensing that they are somehow different. They have been hurt by those who laughed, or scolded.

Perhaps I could tell it best by simply describing some impressions of an evening when I invited ten of these people to eat together and talk. They brought some of their friends.

Here is what happened.

As people were arriving, I noticed that those who had come first were nudging each other and commenting on those arriving.

"Oh! She has a nice halo," a nurse on my right said.

"What's a halo?" I asked.

The nurse looked at me, a little bewildered, and said, "You know, an aura."

"What's an aura?" I asked.

"You can't see auras?" she asked, as though she were a little sorry.

"See what?" I persisted.

My friend from the university, sitting to my left, said, "Come on, Hutchinson, you know what a halo is."

"You mean those brass rings," I said, a bit peeved, "those brass rings the painters of the Middle Ages put above the saints."

"Well, you know," he said, patiently, "those gold rings were a convention--a conventional way for artists to depict in paint what can't be depicted on canvas."

"All right," I said, "I've heard of halos, and I've heard of auras. What do they look like? What do you see?"

"You have one," the nurse said, directing her gaze up at something above my forehead.

"What's it like?" I asked, a little nervously.

"Don't worry," said a nightclub singer who sat on the other side of the nurse. "Yours is a nice one."

"You could be a healer," said the nurse.

"That's good," I said, "I'm for that."

"It's gold and white," the nurse said.

The night club singer nodded. They agreed, then.

"What other colors are there?" I asked.

"Green, and red, and.." The nurse was groping for words as she looked around the table. I had the feeling she was surveying the colors of those who sat with us at the huge round table.

"And black," said the singer.

"Yuk," said the nurse, "black. That's an awful one. I've only seen one black halo and I never want to see another."

"You're ahead of me," I interrupted. "You said green. What's with a green halo?"

"Haven't you heard of someone being 'green with envy?'" asked the singer.

"Yes," I said cautiously. I didn't want to get trapped some way. And, above all, I didn't want my nice gold and white halo to shift on me with all these sensitive people looking at it. And I was getting jealous of these people who could see things I couldn't see.

"It's more than a saying," muttered the nurse, "because I've seen green auras around jealous people."

"A pukey, okra-chartreuse green," said the singer.

"That's right," said a radio repairman from across the table. "I've seen it."

"Now, how about the black one?" I asked.

"I've only seen one," said the nurse. "A man was brought into the hospital emergency room who had a shimmering black halo. It was awful. I drew back at the sight of him. Fortunately other nurses were there. I don't know if I could have taken care of him at that point--I suppose I could.

"One of the staff people said this man had been in the county jail and had tried to burn the jail down. He was being brought in for burns."

The nurse shuddered involuntarily.

"How about the red halo?" I asked.

Several people around the table spoke of the red halos they'd seen. They were anger signs. But, again, it was the nurse from my right who gave the answer I remember best.

"Being able to see halos," said the nurse, "has been very helpful to me. For example, we have a head nurse who has a vile temper. I am the only one on the floor who hasn't had a run-in with her. The reason, I'm sure, is that whenver I see that head nurse coming down the hall with red glowing around her head, I get really busy in some other part of the floor."

A lady farther down the table said to me, "Duane, you're a minister. I hope you won't take offense at this. One of the easiest places to see halos is in church."

Several around the table nodded in agreement.

"Why is that?" I asked. "All saints aside."

"Because," she said, "when you're sort of half asleep during the sermon--just sort of peaceful like and could doze--that's when you can see best."

"Then you're talking about a different kind of seeing," I said.

More nods around the table. But they weren't nodding off to sleep. Everyone was leaning forward with excitement. And, we were also hungry and waiting for our orders to come.

"When you're peaceful like that," said the nurse, "then. . ."

"Alpha state," whispered my friend from the university.

". . .then you see the halos all over the church."

I leaned back. My salad was coming. "I'm sure Saint Peter would be pleased about that," I said. "Halos all over the church." I hoped I didn't offend anyone by seeming not to take it all seriously. I was actually taking it so seriously that I had to back off now and then and joke a little for relief.

As we ate that evening, I was pleased to see the eager, almost childlike excitement of those who had gathered. They were sharing childhood experiences, too.

The nurse, next to me, who was most articulate, told of having an "imaginary friend." "But to me," she said, "he was not imaginary. He was very real. But my mother and father made me give him up, or rather, give up saying anything about my friend."

Others agreed. They had been scolded and spanked for persisting in their "imaginary" friendship.

"And another thing," said the nurse, "I felt kind of lonely and different when I found out that other kids couldn't get outside of themselves. For example, we went to a big stone church. It had windows high off the floor. The walls were thick, so the window shelf was deep.

"I loved to sit up on that shelf and look at the back of my dress. One Sunday morning I had a new dress with a big red bow on the back. My hair hung down my back to that bow. One Sunday morning I was up there on the window shelf looking down at the back of my dress. I tried to get the other kids to do that too, but they acted like they didn't know what I was talking about."

"I don't either," I had to confess. "You mean, your body was down on the floor, and yet you were somehow up in the window looking down at your body?"

"Yes," she said. "I guess they call it an out-of-body experience nowadays, but I didn't know what to call it. I just knew I could do it and the others couldn't. That was something else I learned not to talk about."

At times during that meal, I had to pinch myself to see if I were really a normal thinking person, that my mind was working as I was used to having it work. I felt a little like being in another culture and I was the odd person. There is value in being a minority for awhile, because it gives one compassion for others, but at moments I wondered if it was worth it.

One thing I was sure of was that this was a group of people who were enthusiastic about being together. They were picked because they had had vivid ghost stories to tell me at some time during that previous year. But I found out that these people had a lot more in common. And in pouring out their stories of their frustrated childhoods I felt that the whole enterprise was a good thing.

In fact, I thought of an analogy. What if only one in a thousand people could see colors? Wouldn't they have a difficult time trying to explain a sunset to everyone else? Wouldn't they be abused and jeered on the schoolground? "Oh, look at that red bird!" Yet, they wouldn't even be able to do that, because there wouldn't be a word for red. Wouldn't they be told to give up their foolishness? It probably wouldn't be pleasant and people such as these gathered here would learn to keep quiet about what they could see. And what a pity! We could all learn so much.

Toward the end of the evening the group started talking about ghosts or, as they often put it, "entities." Some were evil and frightening. Some were merely nuisances. Some were positively friends.

Again, my favorite spokesperson for that evening was the nurse at my right. Here's what she said:

One day I was working at the hospital and I had a feeling that something was wrong at home. I couldn't throw off the feeling. My two junior high daughters were home alone. I had told them they weren't to leave the house or have any friends over except for the two girls next door. Certainly no boy friends.

My uneasiness grew until I gave in to the feeling and called home. When no one answered, I became frightened. They were not supposed to be away from the house.

I took off work, something I rarely did, and raced home. When I walked into the house I saw my two girls and two neighbor girls all hunched over the dining room table. Hovering above the center of the group was a--I didn't think 'demon' so much as some creature from outer space. There was definitely an entity there.

As it hovered, it seemed to have the girls in its control. I screamed at it: "In the Name of Jesus Christ, get out of here!"

It shot over to the corner of the room and hovered there, but it wasn't leaving. The girls still cowered at the table. They hadn't even looked at me once--weren't even aware I was in the house, though I know I called their names.

I ran into the bedroom and got my rosary and my prayer book. I came back and repeated the command: "In the name of Jesus, get out." I read from the book and prayed for deliverance.

Like a flash it left. When it left, the four girls slumped over the table like they had been dropped off strings. They all began crying. My daughters looked up at me for the first time, jumped up from the table and ran to me and hugged me.

"Oh, Mother! Oh, Mother! Thank God you've come. We were so scared."

"What happened? What happened?"

They couldn't talk for crying.

"What have you done?" I wanted to know, and then I saw it. The Ouiji Board was on the table.

Little by little, they got it out. They had been playing with the Ouiji Board and it got to talking to them and then it seemed as if they froze. They couldn't move. They did know something had them in its grips. They had not seen anything, but they had felt imprisoned.

"What was it?" I asked.

"I'm not sure," said the nurse. "I wouldn't call it a demon. As I say, it was more like some little entity from outer space. All I know is, I didn't want it in the house and the girls didn't either.

"And I can tell you this," she went on, "the girls burned that Ouiji board in the burning barrel in the back of our lot that afternoon and I've never had any trouble with the girls asking to get another."

## SOUTH BRANCH BOOK CLUB

Kids often yell out, "Shut out the lights," when they hear there is going to be a ghost story. But I have trouble telling any kind of a story in the dark. I need to see people's faces. It makes a lot of difference to me whether people look like they're interested or wish I'd drop the whole thing.

Anyway, some ghosts appear in broad daylight. Take this one, for example.

Helen Kimbahl had passed seventy now and didn't like it a bit. She originated the South Branch Book Club. She started off with eleven charter members in 1959.

But then, Nellie died. Her sister, Rose, died a few weeks later--those two never could stand to be apart for long. Elvina Walker moved to Phoenix with her husband. She said she'd come back, but she never did. Vera Robinson moved to her daughter's in Florida. Helen took each loss as if it were a personal affront.

Eleanor had reviewed Alexander Solzhenitsyn's Cancer Ward only two months ago, and then she herself died of the quick cancer only three weeks later. It threw a gloom over the whole group. Seven ladies still belonged to the South Branch Book Club.

But you might as well say there were only six since Jessica was so crippled in the joints and hardly able to remember her own name. Helen Kimbahl reviewed Kubler-Ross's On Death and Dying in February. She said it would be good for the group, and it was.

Now, it was already March. The first-Tuesday-of-the-month brunches seemed to roll around faster and faster.

When Helen Kimbahl arrived, she nodded briefly to the group members and walked straight back to the bathroom.

During the cinnamon wafers and coffee, Sadie asked if some one should check on Helen.

At last Brunch was finished, dishes stacked and the program ready to start, but no Helen Kimbahl.

Ruth said, "When I complimented her on the presentation last time she only nodded and smiled faintly. She wanted to keep to herself and the group members were thoughtful enough to let her do so--would for awhile, anyway. Helen could be kind of moody at times."

One of the ladies went to check on Helen and found the bathroom empty. The door was open. No one there.

Some went to windows to see if Helen's Oldsmobile was out front. No Olds. Others called upstairs.

Then the phone rang. It was Helen's neighbor, Frank Salzman. He said, "Didn't you hear? Helen Kimbahl was hit at the crossroads on the way to the club meeting. That was an hour ago. Truckload of cattle. She died instantly, they thought. "

She hadn't been at the meeting at all!

## A CASE OF EXORCISM?

Late one March night, I came home from a storytelling tour. I was tired and looking forward to sleeping in the next morning. I had no more than hit the mattress when the phone rang beside my bed.

I don't like to hear the phone ring near midnight. It generally means trouble. However, I had received many night calls while at the university and had a phone by our bed. When I picked up the receiver I half expected to hear a wailing voice on the other end of the line saying, "Oh, oh, I've broken up with my boyfriend and I don't have anybody to talk to."

It was a woman's voice all right, and its urgency brought me fully awake. "Help! For God's sake can you help?"

"What's wrong?" I asked.

"There's something in this house I don't understand. We can't see it, and yet it's trying to touch us. My husband and I are scared to death, but we can't afford to move."

"How did you get my name?" I asked.

"I called the university. They said you do something about things like this." Her voice was turning into a wail.

"I don't do anything about it," I said, "but I do like to collect the stories. . uh . . in the daytime. Couldn't we talk in the morning?"

"But, it's been happening tonight again," she said. "Do you know where I can get help?"

"Well," I said, "there is a group out in Western Nebraska that goes to places like this. They're a Christian group of psychics. They go where there's trouble, and pray, and after they are through there isn't any more problem. It sort of 'clears the air' I guess."

I could hear heavy breathing on the other end of the line.

"They don't charge anything," I said, reassuringly.

"Please," she whispered, "can you get me in touch with them?"

"First," I said, "would you tell me a little of what is going on so I can explain it to them? Would you tell me your name?"

She said, "I'm Kim Kerska. Last October when my husband and I and our two little girls moved into this house near South Street, we noticed how noisy the neighbors were upstairs. They'd walk around all night, or go running up and down the outside stairway next to our bedroom wall.

"We were glad when we heard they were moving out November 30th. We looked forward to some rest. But, after they moved out and no one else moved in, the noise continued! We would hear the pacing around above our ceiling and people running up and down the stairway outside our bedroom wall.

"Lenny, my husband, would go outside with a flashlight to see who was running up and down the stairs--and there wouldn't be anybody. Yet, all the time while he was out looking, I could hear the steps.

"Then, in January I noticed that our girls, Lenita and Trish, started talking in their sleep. That was something they had never done before. I went in the first time and found them sitting up on their bunk beds just talking away to somebody I couldn't see. They were looking away from me at the blank wall.

"I said, 'Nita! Who are you talking to?'

"Nita paid no attention to me. She went on talking. I went over and shook her shoulders. I said 'Nita! Who are you talking to?'

"Nita woke up then, looked at me a second and then fell back exhausted in bed. She said, 'Mommy, why did you wake me up?'

"I said, 'You were talking. Who were you talking to?'

"'I wasn't talking to anybody. You woke me up.' Then she rolled over and went back to sleep.

"It got so this would happen night after night. The girls would talk--not to each other but as if someone else were in their bedroom with them. I'd go in, shake them awake, and then they'd go back to sleep. They wouldn't remember anything about it the next morning--except that I had awakened them. They'd complain about that.

"Then one night in February, I went back in our bedroom to get a towel--we have a linen closet in there--and I hesitated at the door. I just _knew_ somebody was in that bedroom, and that it wasn't any of us.

"I peeked in and there I could see the impression of someone sitting on our bed! The bedclothes were simply pressed down and the mattress dented in like someone was there--but there wasn't. I ran screaming for Lenny. He went into the bedroom and then he called me.

"'Come here,' Lenny said.

"I didn't want to go in, but I came anyway. Lenny was standing on the other side of the bed and I could see now that the deep impression on the bed had moved over to the far side.

"Lenny was standing there holding his hand in the air about two feet above the bed. 'Come here,' he said, 'I want you to feel how cold it is.'

"I came around the bed next to Lenny and put my hand where he said, and it was just like putting my hand in the refrigerator. Pull my hand away and it was warm, push it back in that space and it was cold.

"I said, 'Lenny, I don't like it. Let's get out of here.' But we can't afford to move. Lenny has been laid off work for two months and my little salary doesn't go very far.

"Then one night our friend Al Holtz was over. We'd been telling him about it and how we could find that cold place in different parts of the room. Al was looking for a cheap place to live because he was laid off the same time as Lenny. You see, we've known Al for a long time. In fact, he's the one who introduced us before we were married.

"We said, 'Al, why don't you come over and live in our basement. There's a fold-out couch down there and it's always warm in the basement.'

"So, Al moved in with us the first of March. It felt good to have somebody else around the house. He's really good with our girls too.

"But then, one night, we were just bedding down when we heard this goshawful scream coming up the basement stairs. Here came Al, three steps at a time. His face was white. He was wringing his hands.

"Al said, 'There's somethin' down there.' He pointed back at the basement door. It touched my hand.' He rubbed the back of his hand. He said, 'I was just going to sleep and I heard the basement door. I looked up and could see the doorknob turning back and forth. I thought it was one of you guys. But when the door swung open I could see there wasn't anybody there.

"'I had my hands outside the covers, when somebody laid a cold hand across the back of my hand. Yuk! It was real gentle, but golly I came up out of that bed so fast. I made those nine steps in three. Man! I'm gonna get my sleeping bag and sleep up here in the dining room.'

"So, he did, and Al has been sleeping up here ever since."

"Why did you call me tonight?" I asked.

She said, "Because that thing, whatever it is, was in our bedroom again. I felt something touch the back of my hand and the first thing I thought of was a cat. But we don't have any cats anymore.

"We've all been in the dining room until I called you just now. Can't you do something, please?"

I said, "Mrs. Kerska, I'll call one of the members of this group--it's too late tonight, even out in Ogallala--but I'll call out tomorrow. In the meantime you try to get some sleep, okay?"

I got her off the line and sat back on the edge of the bed. The "group" I had told her about had come to my attention four years earlier. The minister of one of the largest churches in Lincoln had invited me to one of their church family camps out at the edge of the Rocky Mountains. I'd told a few ghost stories one night, and he said, "Duane, if you want to hear some ghost stories, you should talk to Rev. Rose, one of our ministers out in Western Nebraska. He gave the name of the town. He said, "I stopped in there to visit this old minister thinking I'd probably stay fifteen minutes, and I stayed two hours. Rose is fascinating and he's right down your alley with these stories you've been collecting."

It happened that a few months later I was driving through Rev. Rose's town and I stopped in to talk. I took my tape recorder and I stayed over two hours--until I ran out of tape and also knew I wouldn't make it home until past midnight.

"We call our group 'The Soul Rescue Mission,' the old clergyman said. "We're made up of all different groups--Protestants, Catholics. There are clergy and laymen and lay women. But everyone is psychic and we're all in the fellowship of 'The Brother.'

"Who is that?" I asked.

Rev. Rose looked away for a moment. "It would be difficult to explain," he said, "unless you were one of us. The Brother is . . . on the other side.

"What do you do?"

"We pray for one another, support each other. We pray for others and support who we can. And then, of course, there are the missions.

"The missions?" I asked.

"Well," he said, "let's say there is a house out here in Sheridan County where things are going bump in the night. People know about us. They get in touch. We find out all we can, meet and pray about it and follow the leading of the Spirit. Generally we can tell when we meet if the entity in the house is evil or harmless. If we think it will be a threat, several of us will go at once--after prayer."

"What do you do?" I asked.

"We go in. We generally can tell right away something about it, whether it was a man or woman in this life. But we talk to the people first and ask where it makes itself known.

"And," he went on, "it's a funny thing. Often the people will try to deceive us. We'll ask where and they'll say, maybe, 'It's the stairway. We hear it coming down the stairway.' And they'll point upstairs.

"We'll walk around until we find an assurance of where it is. There is usually a locus--a place where its power is more present than elsewhere. We find, for example, that the locus is back in the kitchen, next to the basement stairway. We'll walk back and forth through the spot until we're sure and then say something about it. "'This is where it is, isn't it? Not the front stairway upstairs, but this one going down to the cellar?'

"One man clapped his hands over his mouth and said, 'Oh, m'gosh! How did you know that?"

"I said to him, 'Why did you say it was the front stairs?'

"He said, 'Because I didn't believe you could do it. I guess I didn't think you were on the level.'

"Once we win their confidence we can be of help to them and they to us.

"We go into meditation then, get really quiet, until we are in touch with the person who is there, or persons. Sometimes it is more than one. We ask what is troubling them and why they don't go on over to the other side. We pray for them and calm them and help them get over. Once they are over on the other side they won't trouble the house any more."

"What do you mean by 'the other side,'" I asked, not sure I wanted to know.

Rev. Rose went on. "Different communions call it by different names. The Catholics speak of Purgatory, a place of purgation and cleansing. It is a stopping place of cleansing on the way to the other side.

"Sometimes when there is a sudden death, or a violent death, the person has not had time to prepare. He or she doesn't even know what's happened. He or she keeps trying to get back into this life. This, I believe, is why people feel cold before they see an entity. It is as though that entity were trying to draw heat out of you in order to take form again."

"It makes me shiver," I said.

"Let me give you an example," said Rev. Rose. "Several years ago I was in a parish where a Lutheran minister was quite hostile to me and our Soul Rescue Mission work. He said that I was involved in the occult--devil worship, he called it. I attempted to explain to him that it was just the opposite. We believe in the Holy Spirit and we serve Jesus Christ as Lord. We go very carefully, asking the Holy Spirit's guidance all the way.

"Well," he said, "I don't like it and believe you should drop it."

"I told him that we believe it is a special calling to those who have a psychic awareness, to be a mission to the troubled who are caught between worlds.

"Still he complained about us.

"Then one day I heard that the Lutheran minister's daughter had been hit and killed crossing the highway, coming home after school. I immediately went into prayer. Then the phone rang. It was that minister, asking me to pray for his daughter. He said, 'I apologize for everything I've said about you. I have this terrible feeling that --its not only that Amy was killed, I can feel an agony in her soul. Something is very wrong. I don't know how to say it. Please pray for us."

"I promised I would and went into prayer. Then I rose and went out to the highway where she had been hit. The ambulance had left over an hour before, but there were still police there with tape measures, measuring skid marks, and people standing around.

"I didn't find her there. I usually find them hovering right over the spot where their soul and body were separated. I continued in prayer and the next day went to the funeral home. There I found her, hovering right above her casket.

"I prayed and spoke to her in that inner way. She wouldn't answer. When I left I said, 'I keep praying for you, that you may get over to the other side. There is no future for you here.'

"When I came back the next day she was still hovering there, about three feet above her casket. 'Why are you here?' I asked her.

'You need to get over to the other side.'

"She wouldn't answer, so I left promising her that I would continue to pray for her until she got over.

"It was a huge funeral. All the school children came and there weren't nearly enough seats for everyone inside. The rest of the crowd stood outside and heard the service over temporary loud speakers.

"I sat about twenty feet from the casket, just behind the family. I could tell she was still hovering above her casket. I projected thoughts of the love of God to her. It was a celebration of faith, that service was.

"We went to the graveyard--a chilly afternoon in April. She continued to hover above her casket after it was lowered. After the committal service, I projected thoughts to her and told her I would continue to pray for her and come back in the evening.

"That April night, I drove out to the cemetery. She was still there above her grave. I spoke to her in my heart and asked her, 'Why? Why are you still here? Your parents believe in God. They have celebrated their faith, and they have given you in love to heaven.'

"She spoke to me for the first time. She didn't speak as you and I would speak with so many words, but she was definitely sending me a message. She was saying, 'I can't bear to leave my parents.'

"I said, 'You will be with your parents more quickly if you get on over to the other side. There is no time there. The instant you get over, they'll be there, even if they live to be a hundred.'

"And, the next moment she was gone. I thought perhaps she had made it over to the other side.

"I walked back across the cemetery, that chilly April night. When I got to my car I found her. She was hovering above the radiator in a way that made me think she was trying to draw heat from it.

"'What are you doing here?' I asked, almost sharply. 'There is no future for you here. Your parents trust God. They have committed you to God.'

"She said, 'I can't leave my friends at school.'

"I said once more, 'Your friends are way ahead of you. They trust in God. They have given you to God. Once you get over to the other side you'll be with them. Instantly. There is no time on the other side.'

"At once she was gone. And the immense feeling of relief that went with her going, made me sure she had made it over to the other side.

"I jumped into my car almost jubilantly. I drove back to town and went immediately to the telephone to call the girl's father--the Lutheran minister. But then I hesitated. It was past ten o'clock. He had had a hard day.

"But while I hesitated, my phone rang. I picked it up. It was the Lutheran minister. He had joy in his voice. 'Thank you! Thank you,' he said. 'I've just had the most restful feeling of relief. It happened about a half an hour ago. I feel that everything is all right with my daughter now. Where were you? I tried to call.'

"'I was out at the graveside,' I told him, 'praying.'

"And when I told him everything that happened, as well as I could, he said, 'That's it! I'm sure that's it!'

"From that time since, that Lutheran minister has been my friend. He will often say, 'I don't understand what you are doing, but I'm for you. I believe what you are doing is of the Holy Spirit.'"

That visit, as I said, with Rev. Rose, went on for two hours, until I felt I must leave to make the eight-hour trip back to my home in Lincoln. I must confess that most of what he told me went completely over my head. In fact, I was so freaked out by much of what he said, that I have not even to this day listened to the whole tape of that conversation.

A year or so later he came to my aid. A former student of mine, now in her first teaching job, called me one day, long-distance. She needed help for one of her third graders, she said.

When I asked her what the problem was, she told how she had put on a little Halloween Party for her children. "I asked them if they would like to tell some scary or spooky thing that had happened to them. Each of the children related some little experience--being frightened by a jack-o-lantern, or a cow in the pasture, or their big brother telling a scary story.

"Then," she said, "we came to one little third grade girl who told a story that was so frightening that I took her to the principal's office. The principal tape recorded her story. There is something horrible going on in her home. I know you have been collecting these ghost stories. Can you help?"

I said, "I can't help, I just write down the stories. But there is a group out in Western Nebraska. . ."

At her urging I called Rev. Rose who had held me enthralled during a long conversation. He said, "As a matter of fact, one of our group members lives just twelve miles from your teacher's school. He's a fine Catholic layman and has good sense about him. I'll call him."

So, Rev. Rose called his group member, at no expense to me. A few days later he called me back and gave me a report. He said, "John went over to the school, checked out the situation with them. Visited with the school psychologist, then visited the little girl's home. When he found that the home was not cooperative, he reported back to the school and dropped the whole matter.

When I talked to the teacher later, I found her to be impressed by the careful way in which the gentleman had gone about the investigation. The school then took up the problem with the home.

Now, here I was after two more years and needing the group again, for Lenny and Kim Kerska. I called out to my minister friend in Western Nebraska. He asked a number of questions. When he was satisfied we had a case worth looking into, he said, "Our regional group will meet Monday night for our regular prayer session. I'll propose we take up the matter and find out who's troubling the house."

I said, "You mean you'll drive down to Lincoln?"

"Oh, no," he said, "we don't need to be on the location."

"You'll need the name and address, I suppose." I had been hesitant to give it out.

"No," he said, "just the first names and the general area of Lincoln.

The next Monday night I had a phone call. Rev. Rose said, "We have met and found out who is bothering Lenny and Kim and tell them not to worry. It's an uncle of hers who died last October. He is harmless. He's trying to help, actually, but it only frightens her."

"I see," I said, but I didn't see. I had a funny feeling that goose pimples were rising under my collar when he said this. I'm not used to this kind of talk.

"We think the name is Byron Jennings, but we aren't sure."

"I see. I'll tell her," I said.

The next night I called the Kerskas. Lenny answered and I explained it to him as best I could. When I talked to her she said, "Oh, they're wrong. I didn't have any uncle die last year."

So, I called Western Nebraska again and told Rev. Rose.

The minister said, "We goofed, I guess. We miss sometimes. But, it's funny. We had quite a concensus among us--Byron Jennings. We'll continue to pray."

Thursday night I had a call from Kim. She was angry. "I'm so mad," she said.

"Are you mad at me?" I asked.

"No," she snapped. "I'm mad at my mother."

"Why do you tell me?"

"Because I just reached my mother down in Shreveport. I've been trying to call her for three days. I told her about those people and how they thought I had an uncle who died last October.

"And Mom said, 'Well, of course. There was your Great Uncle B. J. Stevens down in Southern Louisiana. He died last fall. But I didn't think you'd remember him. He only visited us up in Nebraska one time and you were so small.'

"'But, I do remember him!' I said. 'Isn't he the man who used to whistle all the time?'

"'Yes, he did whistle. I remember that too.'

"'He'd set me on his lap and I'd get him to whistle. He peeled an apple for me once.'

"'Yes. My goodness! You do have a memory--you couldn't have been three, hardly. But, he did take a liking to you. Though, he never did visit us again. When I heard from one of the cousins, about his death last fall, I guess I just didn't get around to letting you know. Uncle B. J. was really Byron Jennings Stevens. He was on my grandmother's side."

I called Western Nebraska again--I was getting quite a phone bill by this time--and said, "I guess we're back in business."

I went ahead and gave Rev. Rose's name and phone number to Kim. Friday night I had a call from her. She said, "Three of the group are going to come to Lincoln next Monday night. They had a water department meeting in Omaha the next day. They'll stop on the way about seven o'clock. Can you come?"

"Oh, gee whiz, no!" I said. "That's not my kind of thing. Anyway I have an engagement to speak at a Young Authors' Conference at Raymond that night. You'll get along all right. They're nice people."

Next Monday night I had barely gotten up from the supper table when the phone rang. It was Kim again. She said, "I've just had a call from Kearney, a hundred and fifty miles west of here. They're on their way. They've had car trouble, but they have it fixed and are on their way. They plan to be here by eleven. Are you free then?"

I said, "Well, yes, I mean no, I mean, I should be back from my Young Authors' Conference by then, but really I'm not the sort of person. . ."

"Oh, please come," she said.

I felt a rush of guilt. After all, I thought, I had gotten her into it in a way. So I said, "All right. I'll come."

My wife said, "Duane! What are you agreeing to?"

I explained and went out the door to the Young Authors. It was hard to keep my mind on what I was trying to say to the kids, thinking about what was awaiting me at eleven o'clock.

I drove up to the house near South Street at exactly eleven. I could see three people up on the porch talking to the lady of the house. I went up and found them introducing themselves all around.

I noticed one of the men put out a cigarette. He had a deeply wrinkled face like a recovered alcoholic I once knew. The lady with him, who was introduced as his girlfriend, looked like she had retired from a career in a night club. I thought, in a self-satisfied sort of way, "These people aren't very spiritual."

The third person was tall and had a well-groomed appearance and brushed thick white hair. He made me think of my imaginary picture of St. Peter.

We walked on in, paused in the living room and heard the group members saying, "We should have the meeting in the basement. That's where the locus is."

I turned to the young husband, Lenny, and said, almost desperately, "Why don't I look after your girls, and _you_ go on down to the basement?"

"Oh, no!" Lenny said. "That's not my kind of thing. I'll stay up here and _you_ go down."

So I went down. Skeptic that I was, I found myself counting the steps. There were nine. I turned around and looked at the doorknob. I recalled that the friend had seen the door knob turning and I had wondered when I heard it how he could see a round door knob turn in poor light. But there was illumination from an alley light which fell on the door, and the knob was oval shape, like a tiny football. Of course he could see it wigwag.

We sat in the basement. The furniture down there looked like it had been through Goodwill twice. The alcoholic and the nightclub singer sat on the sofa to my left. St. Peter (not his name) sat on a folding chair opposite me. Then Kim, the little housewife and mother, sat at my right. I comforted myself thinking "those people are only giving her a little help cleaning house."

I said to the group, "I brought my tape recorder. I want it on so if I go into a trance or something, ha, ha, I can still know everything that was said."

The alcoholic (I'm being so unfair. He was probably a teetotalling Sunday School teacher) said, "Oh, that's all right about the tape recorder. We brought ours too."

He lifted out an expensive-looking piece of equipment from his satchel. It sort of showed up my little K-Mart twenty-dollar special.

"It's voice actuated," he said, "so we don't waste tape and batteries during long silent periods. Sometimes a voice comes through that we can't understand immediately and then we can study it later."

Now St. Peter spoke. "We will join hands in a circle and pray," he said, "each supporting the other with your right hand."

I remember I had to turn over my right hand, palm up, so I would be supporting Kim beside me.

"Now, as we meditate and get in touch with the entity that is here in the house, you may see him appear in the center of the group. Don't be frightened. We don't think he is evil. But, if you do think you have reason to be afraid, if he threatens you, hold a cross between you and the center."

I frantically tore my hands loose and searched my pockets. "I don't have a cross on me," I thought.

But, I took hands again, and we began. Each said a short prayer and mine was, "Almighty God, unto whom all hearts are open, all desires known, and from whom no secrets are hid, cleanse the thoughts of our hearts by the inspiration of Thy Holy Spirit that we may perfectly love thee and worthily magnify thy holy name, through Christ our Lord. . .and. . . (I continued silently) forgive me for getting caught in a jam like this."

We were completely silent for awhile, and then I noticed that Alcoholic on my left was breathing rather regularly. In fact, in a moment I could distinctly hear the beginnings of a snore.

I thought, "Oh, for heavens sake! What am I doing down here at midnight listening to some guy from Western Nebraska snore?

But, then St. Peter spoke sharply. "Wake up!"

Alcoholic woke up with a start. "Oh, I'm sorry," he said. "I'm so tired. Let's try again."

I felt more compassionate, thinking about these people who, at my request, had driven out of their way to help a stranger--and at their own expense. But for me they could have been asleep in their motel by now.

I felt compassionate right up until he started to snore again. St. Peter spoke sharply again. "Wake up!"

There were snuckles deep in Alcoholic's throat, somewhere between an interrupted snore and a gargle. "I'm sorry," he said. "Let's try again."

We sat in silence. Kim's lips were moving.

Just when I thought Alcoholic would start to snore again, something happened for which I was not prepared. Old Alcoholic began to rise off the sofa, a little gargling sound came from his throat, and then he began to speak in well-modulated tones and perfect university English. I think I know a little bit about linguistics, having scraped my way through a course in it once, and I would say that this man from Western Nebraska was definitely not talking "country" as he had when I met him on the porch.

The voice was speaking now rhythms which made me think of the psalter. The voice was speaking beautiful blank verse. The tone was gentle and the words were consoling. "Your uncle is not able to speak, but I, The Brother, will tell you of his concern. You have not been to church for a long time. You need to strengthen your faith. Your husband is under temptation, but with your help he will be well."

The voice went on, surrounding me like a gentle symphony. At last it came to a stop and I could see Alcoholic straining to purse his lips, his eyes closed, his face turned upward.

St. Peter clapped his hands and I started from my chair. "Wake up," St. Peter said. "Wake up!"

Alcoholic fell from his upraised position, fell out of his trance. The wrinkles came back into his face. "I'm sorry," he said, "I guess I'm just too tired to be of much help."

"No," said his nightclub girlfriend, "we got it."

"We have the message," said St. Peter.

"Oh, thank God," said Alcoholic. "Now, we can go home."

The young woman beside me was ecstatic, clapping her hands. "That was him, that was my Uncle B. J. It was so good to hear his voice again after all these years. And he said just what I needed to hear. I have been away from church, because I thought we were too poor. But now I'm going to start back. I had stopped believing anything really good. My husband has been having some problems, but it's going to be different now."

Then, it seemed, everyone was talking at once. It was like after the game, everyone was going over positions and plays.

I wanted out. I was already heading for the stairs. I started counting steps again and said to myself, "Stop it!"

Upstairs they had to go over the whole thing with the husband and the friend. The girls were long asleep.

Out on the porch, as we were leaving, Alcoholic swung around and gave me a peculiar look. He looked straight into my eyes, gently touched my chest, and said, "Baltimore."

I said, "What about it?"

"Baltimore, Maryland."

"Yes," I said, "Baltimore is in Maryland." I felt like I was speaking to a child.

But Alcoholic continued to gaze at me with what seemed to me an intense but kindly gaze. "Why do I think 'Baltimore' and some sadness when my mind is directed to you? Do you know something about Baltimore?"

"No," I said, lying.

His shoulders slumped. His face relaxed. He looked years older. "Sometimes I'm wrong," he said, and turned to go down the walk.

I thought, here are these tired people, they've driven hundreds of miles today, they've come to help others and they aren't asking anything. Alcoholic wasn't asking anything just then, except an honest answer, and I didn't give it to him.

"Wait," I said. "Baltimore has been on my mind a lot the last few years. I've written a book about Bishop Otterbein who came and worked Baltimore in the 1700's. I immersed myself in the Chesapeake Bay history until I could stand out on the point where Fort McHenry now is, and I could tell you most of the buildings on the skyline. But, they turned down my book. It won't be published."

"That's it," Alcoholic said with a grin. His eyes twinkled. "Now I can go to bed and get some rest." With a wave he stepped into the car with St. Peter and Miss Nightclub.

I went home too and wished I could rest, but I kept tossing and turning, thinking about the events of the night. "Had I witnessed an exorcism? If so it was gentle and, in a way, beautiful. I fell asleep toward morning thinking, "Whatever was done, it was way beyond me."

And, whatever it was, it must have satisfied Kim and Lenny because I never did hear from them again.

## SCHUYLER GHOST

Several years ago I was invited to Schuyler to tell stories. While there I was lavishly treated with the generosity and affection for which Schuylerites are famous. One of the evenings of that week I was invited to the home of a member of the Arts Council for a party. Thirty or forty of us crowded in, enjoying her lovely restored Victorian home.

I recall that everyone had brought salads or meats or vegetables and desserts. The long table in the dining room was loaded and sumptuous.

After the meal there were some party stunts and much conversation. Somehow the subject of dancing came up. Since they had discovered I liked to dance our hostess suggested rolling back the carpet in the long Queen Anne living room. A relaxed and confident hostess she was!

With the Hi Fi and their favorite dance records, we danced. It was wall-to-wall people, but we danced.

After dancing, we sat around on the carpet and something had happened--none of us wanted to go home. A special atmosphere of intimacy had developed. We talked of personal things. Someone asked me to tell a ghost story, so I did.

After the ghost story our hostess said, in a casual sort of way, "We have one in this house."

Heads turned.

"What did you say, Evelyn?"

"We have a ghost in this house."

"Evelyn!" one of the committee members said. "You've never told us that."

"Well," said Evelyn slowly, "it isn't something you tell. People might think you're. . ." She tapped her temple significantly.

"Why do you think you have a ghost?"

"We just knew." Evelyn looked at her husband. "Didn't we, Dick?"

Dick nodded. "We were over here working several weeks before we moved in. We knew someone else was around."

Silence held us for awhile. The grandfather clock dinged the half-hour in the other room.

We were looking at Evelyn again.

"You know. You just know," Evelyn said. "Little Richard noticed it too and said things."

"What did he say?" I asked.

Evelyn looked at me a moment. I wasn't sure she wanted to go on.

"Well," she said, "one afternoon we were over here--Dick was refinishing the upper mantel. Richard was off in the front bedroom setting up his Christmas blocks and he came tearing in. Pale. Mouth open. I thought he'd swallowed something, at first.

"'Mom, Dad?'

"We said, 'Yes, what is it, Richard?' His eyes were about this big." Evelyn held her fingers up in circles.

"'Mom, Dad,--there's somebody else in this house isn't there?'

"I looked at Dick. Dick looked at me. We didn't want to lie to our own son. 'Well, yes, we've felt that sometimes.'

"Richard relaxed right away and went back to playing. We never could get it out of him why he said that.

"Oh," she said, "I can tell you about the night we all knew it for sure. We were watching TV here in the living room and Bobo started to growl, an eerie, dreadful growl. He stood up and the hair came up on his back. We thought he was going for the door but he ran to the stairway.

"Bobo knew he was not to go up the stairs, but he was so excited he ran up a few steps, ran down, and ran up again.

"Dick bounded up those stairs two at a time. He looked all over, but didn't find anybody."

Evelyn stopped for a moment.

We all looked to the stairs. An elaborate letter S was carved into the newel post. Lovely carved oak ballustrades framed the stairway. A portion of the tall palladian window at the landing showed from where we sat.

"It was unsettling," said Dick. "I knew someone was there on the landing and I could feel the cold. Bobo looked right at it, but I couldn't see a thing."

"Soon after this," Evelyn said, "I began walking in my sleep. Never had I sleepwalked before. But now I'd get up and somehow walk all the way across the hall, past the stairs, past Richard's room and into the guest room at the back. I'd wake up on the guest bed, freezing.

"Dick developed the habit of jumping up any time I got up in the night, to make sure I was awake.

"Then," Evelyn continued, "I contracted a horrid fear of the stairs--afraid some night I'd fall down the steps onto the landing and crash right out that big window."

I had a feeling we were all picturing what she was talking about. We had taken our coats up to the guest room as we arrived. We'd climbed the stairs and turned at the landing with the big window at our backs. The bathroom was straight ahead, the master bedroom was at the left, Richard's room at the right, and the guest room for our coats was on beyond Richard's.

"Dick was good about bouncing up any time I got up in the night," Evelen said, "to be sure I was awake.

"Then, one night I walked in my sleep and Dick didn't hear me. He had been working late several nights. I wakened on the guest room bed. I had taken the mattress off that bed and only spread a coverlet on the springs. I remember feeling the soreness on my back where those springs pressed against me.

"I ran back into our room and woke up Dick. 'You didn't protect me!' I said.

"'Oh, I'm sorry," he said, 'I'm sorry. I was so tired I didn't hear you.'

"The next morning," Evelyn went on, "we were all in the kitchen, getting breakfast. It was one of those mornings when nobody had much to say. We were simply going through the motions.

"Richard sat with one elbow on the table, his cheek in one hand, scooping Cheerios with the other. He looked up and said with a yawn, 'Hey Mom? Who was that man who kept you from falling down the stairs last night?'

"'Richard! What did you say?' I asked.

"'Who was that man who kept you from falling down the stairs?'

"'Your father,' I suppose.

"'No! No!' Richard said. 'This old guy with the funny hat and coat and cane. He stuck out his cane and kept you back from the stairs.'"

Evelyn stopped and we simply sat there--the whole party quiet.

Then, an older member of the Arts Council spoke. She was a distinguished lady who had seen many years of Schuyler's history. "This was the banker's home, you know," she said. "Banker Schulehorn would leave this very front porch every morning at eight-fifteen. We children called him 'Old Schuley.' My mother said she could set the clock by him.

"I can still see Old Schuley taking his walks, wearing his derby hat, horsehair coat, and carrying a marble-topped cane. Richard saw Schuley. But, goodness! Mr. Schulehorn died with the flu in 1918."

A curious thing happened after the party at Schuyler. I went back to Schuyler on another storytelling trip and couldn't recall whose house it was. Even the story, retold in different Schuyler audiences that week, didn't bring any recollections. Edwards didn't fit. Nobody named Evelyn had the party. Was it a different town?

Then, I met a school teacher who said she had told me a similar story at a party when they lived in a big old house in Schuyler, but--oh, my!--it was a different story.

## THE GHOST OF THE MOVING PICTURE

You might think that this is the ghost of the movie house, the cinema phantom, but not so. This was a picture on the wall in an upstairs room in south Lincoln. The picture appeared to move.

Many of the stories that come to me--the stories I like best--come from fairly shy people. This was such a case. This couple, in one of the lovely Victorian mansions near the historic district, told me the story at a party. Over a glass of champagne she told me. I don't think the champagne had anything to do with it. Here's what she said:

We had moved into Geish house June second, and the morning of June third I noticed our bed was out in the middle of the room. Larry said he wasn't that sure we had the bed against the wall, but I was sure we had. True, we had barely moved in and found the box of Wheaties, but the movers had done a good job. Things were basically where I had marked them to be put.

By the next night I had the pictures up in our bedroom. Larry was so exhausted he fell asleep as soon as he hit the bed. But I lay there looking at the big room and thinking about the house. Then I noticed something moving on the wall. What I saw I couldn't believe at first.

The big picture over on the wall, on Larry's side of the bed--that picture was moving steadily to the left. I was frozen at first. Then I punched Larry and whispered, "Look at that picture! It's moving."

Larry stared at it for a moment and then jumped out of bed.

"It's not the picture moving," he said, "it's us!"

We got up and would you believe it? Our bed had moved a good two feet away from the wall. It was as if you're on a train moving out of the station and the depot appears to be moving backward. We were slowly gliding out into the middle of the room, leaving the picture and the wall behind us!

Larry jammed the bed back against the wall and yelled, "Now stay there!"

I had to laugh, the way he said it.

In July my sister Lettie and her husband Frank came from California. They were driving through from coast to coast on Interstate 80 and wanted to see our new/old house.

I frankly wished they would stay at the Cornhusker, but no, she thought it would be a thrill to stay in Geish manor.

We put Lettie and Frank in the big room across the hall from ours, across from the top of the stairway.

"Please! Don't let anything happen tonight," I said to myself. Lettie gets so upset over even small things, and if she heard or saw any of what we'd seen, she'd be down on the house from then on.

Well, it happened. About two o'clock or so I heard them scream. Lettie was screaming, anyway. Frank was yelling something like, "Shoo, shoo!"

They came tumbling out of the room and I hoped they wouldn't fall down the big stairway.

"There's a man in there," Lettie whispered.

"He was standing at the foot of the bed," Frank said. "I woke up and there he was--he was staring at us."

Larry came past me on the double. Frank went back into the room with him to investigate.

Lettie broke into hysterical crying and sagged on my shoulder. "It was awful," she said.

I half carried her into our room.

The men didn't find anything in any of the rooms upstairs and Lettie made Frank take her to a motel that night. She will not have anything to do with my house since that time. She's even turned the rest of my family against our house.

And there are other things. We found our breakfast table set for company one morning. My linens from the dryer were all folded one night. I asked Larry about it, but he didn't know anything about it. He doesn't even know how to fold clothes. Someone else is in the house. I know it. Larry knows it. But, we don't talk about it.

> I thought perhaps this was the end of the story. My friend dabbed at some champagne that had spilled down the front of her dress. I looked around the room. No one was coming to interrupt.

"Then, there are little things," she said, "like ashtrays moving. Then, once the silverware was all out of drawers. Another time a place setting with the soup spoons and everything."

"Good taste," I said.

She looked at me searchingly, seriously. "What do we do? There's someone there."

"Do you have any pets?" I asked.

"No."

"Why don't you get a dog?"
"We just might do that."

I saw her several weeks afterward in Miller and Paine and she said they had indeed gotten a dog, but now wished they hadn't.

"Why?" I wanted to know.

"Because," she said, "we acquired a big Doberman Pinscher from the police department. Supposed to be fearless, they said. But we could not get that dog into any door of the house.

"What happened?" I asked.

"We brought him up on the porch and he began to growl. When we opened the front door he stared at something inside that we couldn't see. His eyes followed something moving. He backed up with a whine, his tail between his legs.

"Larry took him around to the back of the house and couldn't get him in that door either. Larry tried to push him in, but that poor dog went out of his mind.

"I tell you," she said, "there is something wrong in that house. We had to take the dog back to the police department. I can't get any of my family to stay there. Our bed still moves. Sometimes we wake up out in the middle of the room.

"I don't know," she said, "how much longer we are going to stay either, but we have so much invested in the house.

"Why don't you," she said, as if she had just had a bright new thought, "why don't you come and sleep in our guest room? Maybe you can tell us what is going on!"

But so far, my schedule has been so busy, I haven't seen a way to get over there.